THE WEATHERMEN

THE WEATHER MEN

THE WEATHERMEN

their story

GORDON TRIPP
OBE MA

The Book Guild Ltd

First published in Great Britain in 2017 by
The Book Guild Ltd
9 Priory Business Park
Wistow Road, Kibworth
Leicestershire, LE8 0RX
Freephone: 0800 999 2982
www.bookguild.co.uk
Email: info@bookguild.co.uk
Twitter: @bookguild

Typeset in Minion Pro

Printed and bound in Great Britain by
CPI Group (UK) Ltd, Croydon, CR0 4YY

ISBN 978 1911320 425

British Library Cataloguing in Publication Data.
A catalogue record for this book is available from the British Library.

The book is dedicated to my wife Jeanie
for her unfailing support for my interest in the weather.

CONTENTS

PREFACE

One of my earliest memories is of my mother pointing to the sky and telling me of all the different cloud types there were for us to see. Her sense of wonder has remained with me. But as a young man joining the Royal Air Force as a navigator, that wonder had a harder, more practical edge! Flying at high altitude in jet aircraft or spending long hours at low-level over the sea, the weather was, literally, a matter of life and death. Lacking the sophisticated navigation aids that are now available, one had to rely on an understanding of the weather and on the skill of the forecasters on the ground. I was fortunate enough while flying in maritime patrol aircraft to be able to specialise in the subject.

As with many in the military, I was stationed in many parts of the world. From Australia to Germany and from Madagascar to Nigeria, I was able to study the global climate at first hand. After I left the RAF, I worked for a developing world charity and could see, not the impact different climates and weather patterns had on flying operations, but how they impacted directly on the lives especially of the very poor.

It is, perhaps, not surprising then that I have, for

several years, been giving talks and running Adult Education courses on many different aspects of both weather and climate. And we are all endlessly fascinated by these topics. We also love biographies. A popular course, entitled *The Weathermen – Their Story*, brings these two themes together. I have learnt much from the participants – as do all those running courses. Often I have been asked to suggest follow-up reading. There are excellent books available about weather phenomena and there are scholarly and very readable books about individuals who have advanced the art and science of meteorology. What is not so easy to find is a layperson's guide to the overall historical framework within which these advances were made. This book aims to fill the gap. It covers 2,000 years, exploring the many strands which tell the story of weather history – recording instruments, the drawing up of charts, wind circulation, weather diaries, the jet stream and so on. And it is the lives of over 100 people whose biographies provide the signposts along the way. These were essentially men of their times, be that of The Enlightenment, the Crimean War, the days of the British Empire or of two World Wars. As that great scientist Charles Lyell suggested: "It is only by knowing the past that we can know the present and it is only by knowing the present that we can know the future."

ACKNOWLEDGEMENTS

My thanks go to the many members of the staff at the Book Guild for their positive approach to the whole process of producing this book.

To them must be added Duncan Bell at the Met Office Library and Archive and to Jasmine Rodgers at the Science and Society Library for their help in selecting illustrations.

My thanks go to our children Howard, Rachel and Teresa – and their spouses – for their encouragement.

LIST OF ILLUSTRATIONS

1. INTRODUCTION

*Methodology – Difference between
weather and climate – Cast of over 100*

The weather – an endless topic for discussion! And this has always been so. The earliest societies were even more susceptible to its vagaries than we are today. The history of its study thus covers many millennia. There is a timeline that can be drawn for its development, especially in more recent times, but it would include many strands: the development of measuring instruments, production of surface weather charts, the value of ballooning, issuing storm warnings, use of satellites and so on. Each of these topics has its own timeline. So here, rather than staying within the confines of the overall timeline and so shifting from one topic to another and then back again, we follow each theme in turn in this fascinating story of meeting the challenge of understanding the weather.

There is a close relationship between weather and climate. It is best summed up by the well-known aphorism from Mark Twain: "Climate is what you expect, weather is what you get". Climate, by convention, is weather over a period of thirty years. Many climatologists over

1

the years have attempted to establish past climates and to assess what future climate patterns might be. Theirs is a fascinating story, but our focus here is on the lives of meteorologists and the struggles they have had to understand the everyday weather that affects us in the here and now.

The weather of the United Kingdom is complex. The British Isles lie just above the mid-latitudes on the western seaboard of the European land mass and they are subject to prevailing westerly winds coming off the Atlantic Ocean. As a result, this part of Europe experiences ever-changing weather. It is not surprising then that the United Kingdom has produced many of those who helped make major strides in the art and science of weather forecasting. We have here a cast of over a hundred names as shown in the Index of Names; many came from the British Isles.

2. EARLIER TIMES

Setting the scene – Earlier societies –
Greeks, Romans and Chinese – Astrology

THE ANCIENTS

We do not know when the human race started migrating from Africa. The route they took is unclear; indeed there are likely to have been several routes. Doubtless, too, there were waves of movement ebbing and flowing across the generations. Quite why the migrations began gives rise to much speculation; some suggest population growth or competition between slightly different species. For some, changes in climate are seen as a key factor, and the records we now have lend credence to this last view. It is highly unlikely that the arbitrary thirty-year timescale we now use to define climate would have meant much to people struggling year on year to find food and shelter. However, collective memories may well have recalled better, or worse, times, embellished and mystified, just as is done today. But more likely there was just the pressing and immediate imperative for simple survival.

3

Within all this uncertainty one thing is surely clear; then, even more than now, people would have been acutely aware of the weather. Dawn would be a time to view the sky and worry about the day ahead. Would it never rain? Would it never stop raining? Uncommitted to a settled life and fixed location, what hunter-gatherers saw above their heads would dictate the plan for the immediate future. Elders and sages may well have made their inputs and we must assume factors so common to us would have offered clues to them. The colour of the sky, the shape of the clouds, the direction of the wind, the migration of animals, all of these would have been signs with special meanings. Human actions would have been shaped accordingly. In other words, they were weather forecasters. We see examples of this even in recent times. Groups such as the North American Indians live in the most extreme of climates; they have long relied on patterns seen in both flora and fauna to predict the severity of the winter.

And these early humans were part of a species, as we are, which exists within a very narrow band of tolerances to their environment. The conditions within which they could have evolved demanded a temperature range of little more than thirty degrees, levels of oxygen that are found only in the lower few thousand feet of the atmosphere and water available at frequent and regular intervals. Their skills at gathering building materials and making shelters, at producing clothing and in controlling fire, would have gone some way to enlarge the envelope within which they could exist. All these activities underpin the ability, and willingness, to move and expand their living space. It is thus that they met the challenge of the weather.

Many hunter-gatherers may have rested a while in some favourable spot. Reliance on a supply of food, the availability of game and, more than anything else, the proximity of plentiful, clean water, may have caused them to become temporary settlers. Then they would have known the vagaries of the seasons and the changeability of the weather. They would have been able to weigh the advantages of settlement against the freedom of hunter-gathering, of moving on. Plainly many opted for the latter, spurred on, perhaps, by competition for land and resources. But both groups, be they hunter-gatherers or settlers, depended on the weather; the first driven by the seasons, the second fearful of what the seasons might, or might not, bring. To prosper they had to use the weather. Some point to cave paintings from around 15,000 BCE such as those at Lascaux in southern France as evidence that people of those times were acutely aware of the weather. Some images can be interpreted as depicting menacing clouds and heavy rain.

Settled communities such as those in the Fertile Crescent, curving round from Egypt though Mesopotamia to the Persian Gulf, and those in parts of China, thus formed the basis of what was to become the city-state. By around the 6th century BCE the significance of the weather had taken on a different aspect. Agriculture, fishing, travel, shelter, indeed the whole structure of society was built on the weather. At another level, weather events would have been essential omens to be interpreted in terms of political and social actions. This seems to have been the case in parts of early Babylonia. At the same time the skill to guess what tomorrow's

5

weather might bring may well have been the power base for groups of sages, rather like today. We see echoes of this notably among the people of Central and South America where, for the Maya and Inca, the priesthood was seen as providing the essential intermediaries who could negotiate with the gods especially to provide a regular rainfall.

THE GODS OF WEATHER

The link with God or gods is a persistent theme in all forms of weather forecasting. It is worth noting that almost all civilizations have weather gods. Norse, Yoroba, Maori and Aztec all had their own creation stories and their own weather spirits. In the monotheistic religions, God is depicted as the arbiter of the weather, using storms, floods and droughts as punishment meted out to the unrighteous. The biblical Deluge itself, the way it ended, and the escape across the Red Sea, all reflect the sense that there is no value in trying to predict the weather; indeed it is blasphemous to attempt to do so. The New Testament carries this idea forward in the calming of the storm on Lake Galilee. Such was the strength of Christian ideas within western culture that for many, regardless of class, there existed a certainty that God was involved in every aspect of everyday life, rain or shine included. Nor has this concept entirely vanished. As recently as 2015, the appearance of a Blood Moon caused some religious writers to say, "Whatever its significance it seems God knows how to get our attention and we must watch and pray". The constant association of deity and weather can surely be extended back to our very first ancestors. It is little wonder that those closest to nature would have included the controllers of the weather in their pantheon of gods.

RECORDS FROM THE ANCIENT WORLD

Written records of the weather begin to be found in a number of locations starting around the 3rd century BCE. In the Indus Valley the Hindu Upanishad texts examined many topics in the search for truth, including the sciences. Upanishad can be loosely translated as "Sitting beside". These were instructional works explaining the natural world. The water cycle, where water evaporates into cloud and then falls as rain, eventually returning to the sea to start the process again, was recognised, a major stride in understanding the weather and especially the monsoons on which so much depended on the Indian subcontinent. The Babylonians, who made amazing strides in the sciences, also understood the water cycle. Like the Sumerians before them, they were entirely dependent on the flow of the Tigris and Euphrates. Water levels in these rivers were largely seasonal and the pattern of change from year to year formed a basis for knowledge of the climate. There is evidence that, around 650 BCE, they were making efforts to forecast the weather as well. Cloud patterns were seen as significant and what we would now call weather lore, was taken as evidence of the future weather including sayings such as "a dark halo round the moon means rain".

THE GREEKS

As in so many areas of western culture, it is to the Greeks that we turn for the basis of our own thinking about the weather. Thales of Miletus (600 BCE) is usually given pride of place because of his mathematical insights – he correctly explained the reason for eclipses – and his demythologising of natural phenomena. He also understood the water cycle. But it was Aristotle (384-322 BCE) who first used the term *Meteorologie* in his book of that name. It covers a wide spread of natural science subjects including whirlwinds and lightning. His general theory was that winds were exhalations from the earth caused by the sun and, once his works became known in the western world, this idea persisted. It formed the foundation of a book published as late as 1563. In this work, by William Faulke entitled *A Goodly Gallerye*, care was taken to give due primacy to the role of the Christian God but, nonetheless, it was the words of Aristotle that were used. Hippocrates (460-370 BCE) is best known for the eponymous oath taken by medical practitioners, but his writings, notably *Air, Water and Place,* also linked common diseases to particular seasons and winds. This, through the centuries, laid the basis for much of the perceived interaction made between weather, climate and health.

In Egypt the very lives of the people depended on the River Nile, but Greece had virtually no rivers. They thus relied on rainfall, which meant that wind direction was of particular significance. The Tower of the Winds (see Fig 1.), which still stands in Athens, is octagonal and

8

originally included a high level water clock for all to see, and a wind vane. The most likely date of construction was around 50 BCE, though there may well have been a similar tower on the site perhaps 200 years earlier.

Fig 1. Tower of the Winds, Athens

The various winds were part of the pantheon of the gods and each was linked directly to different kinds of weather. This, in turn, impacted on the mood to be expected among the city dwellers. The west wind, Zephyrus, was balmy, the north wind, Boreas, brought winter, Notus, the south wind, meant storms and Eurus was the east wind, which seldom blew. The winds, and hence the weather, were the stuff of myths and legends and attempts to forecast their future direction was treated largely as an irrelevance. All of this was gathered together in their *parapegma* or weather calendar.

THE ROMANS

The realisation that there were various climate zones was part of the Roman achievement. In 25 CE Pomponius Mela produced a map of the world as he saw it with some idea of climatic areas. In many ways the Roman approach to the weather followed that of the Greeks. There is clear commonality in their understanding of the roles of the various wind Gods. It is noteworthy, also, that Jupiter, the supreme god, was also the god of the skies, as was the Greek equivalent, Zeus. Both were often depicted carrying a thunderbolt.

THE CHINESE

China, as far back as 1000 BCE was often run in a highly bureaucratic fashion. Decisions affecting the whole country often had to take into account the weather. For this to be effective, a system of observation stations was set up. Later, Wang Chong (97-27 BCE) wrote critical essays, the *Lunheng*. He noted that rain came from the clouds, not from the interaction of the moon and the stars: "Clouds and rain are the same thing" – a profound realisation. He understood the concept of suspended water droplets; for example, in the mist in mountain passes. Some of his ideas reflect the thoughts of earlier men as codified in the Gongyan Zhuan, which dates from the 2nd century BCE.

ASTROLOGY

For all the societies considered above, weather was seen to have close links with the orbits of heavenly bodies and thus with astrology. Various rules, and later almanacs, would give the best time for sowing or harvesting, aligning the start of the seasons to the juxtaposition of the stars and planets. These prognostications would hold sway for many centuries, in preference to the more tenuous ideas emanating from a slowly growing scientific consensus. Claudius Ptolemy (90-168) was a Greco-Egyptian philosopher best known as a geographer. He produced his own form of *parapegma* and his writings proved influential for many centuries, including his theories concerning astrology and the impact of the heavenly bodies on climate and weather. Later, we have the *Prognosticatio* of Johannes Lichtenberger (1440-1503) published in 1488 and the works of Nostrodamus

(1503-1566). Both of these writers were extremely influential. Closer to home, Thomas Buckminster (1531/2-1599) wrote his own very precise predictions for the year 1598. In these astrological texts we note the linkage between weather and health, both as evidence of the current weather but also as a means of forecasting forthcoming rain or shine. Such interaction was to be a persistent feature over the next 300 years and to an extent remains with us today.

3. MOVING INTO THE SECOND MILLENIUM

Recording weather data – Recording instruments – The Enlightenment – A Time of Melancholy? – Almanac authors and weather wisers – Problems of recording the wind

RECORDING WEATHER DATA

The process of recording weather data in a more systematic and scientific way can be seen to start around the beginning of the second millennium. In the Arab world, men such as Ibn al-Haytham (966-1039) set out a scientific method that he followed especially in the field of optics. He went further and estimated the extent of the atmosphere by measuring the duration of twilight. His figure of about fifty miles high is surprisingly accurate. His approach and that of Ibn Wahshiyya, who produced forecasts based on wind direction, spread through the Mediterranean from Arabia to Iberia in the wake of Islam and impinged directly on the requirement for weather observation records. These certainly existed from around 900 CE onwards with detailed observation concerning the area around Baghdad. There were strong mathematical influences here that were not to impact the western world for many hundreds of years.

The advent of the Little Ice Age, usually dated to run between about 1350 and 1850 CE, stimulated an interest in recording the weather with its bitter winters and times of ruinous rainfall upending the pattern of agriculture that occupied the lives of so many in the population. Among the earliest recorders of the weather we know of in Europe was the Rev William Merle (d1347). Educated at Oxford, he lived in Driby, Lincolnshire. His diary spanned seven years from 1337 to 1344, a time falling broadly during the transition from the Medieval Warm period to the Little Ice Age. We may judge that he was not alone. Certainly, in the 16th and 17th centuries many records were made in the Netherlands, Germany and Italy with this continuing through the 18th century. Several documents have survived and we may reasonably assume there were many more which have now been lost. However, such works were generally descriptive and unquantified; how cold is "very cold"? Moreover, the certainty that bad weather was an expression of God's wrath was, in Europe, all-pervasive. This led to efforts to see, for example, which way lightning forked or where winds blew to better pinpoint the exact target of His displeasure. Quite why benign weather seldom indicated His pleasure is unclear. Graphic pictures were displayed on papers showing the devastating impact especially of floods. We had to wait until well into the 17th century before we could move into the modern era of measuring and recording the weather.

RECORDING INSTRUMENTS

Galileo (1564-1642) and Torricelli (1608-1647) are two names central to this recording process. Galileo is probably best remembered for his dispute with the Roman Catholic Church over the question of whether the sun orbited the earth or whether the opposite was true. His work with telescopes and his identification of sunspots is also well known. However, it was the measurement of temperature that was crucial for meteorologists. The Galileo thermoscope, with coloured spheres in a tube of liquid, makes an attractive contemporary ornament, but his thermometer was of much greater importance. It consisted of a tube in which a liquid rises and falls with changes in temperature. A scale was needed to make the instrument useful and it fell to Fahrenheit in the early 18th century to devise the first standard method of calibrating thermometers.

Daniel Fahrenheit (1686-1736) came from a family of merchants; his parents died from eating poisonous mushrooms when he was fifteen and he started working in Holland as an instrument maker and glass blower. He established a temperature scale with zero as the point where a mixture of water, ice and salts would freeze. Water on its own froze at 32 on this scale and boiled at 212, allowing the mathematically convenient interval of 180 between the two. Many years later the centigrade scale was seen to be more readily understood: it was renamed Celsius in 1948 in honour of the Swedish scientist, Anders Celsius (1701-1744) who had proposed that scale in the early 18th century.

An understanding of atmospheric pressure was

also required, as was a way of measuring it. Torricelli is usually credited with meeting both these challenges. His experimentation was the result of work done to pump water out of mines. He realised that the weight of the air above the earth was constantly varying. The downward pressure it exerted could be measured using a column of mercury and changes in the height of that column noted. Thus was born the mercury barometer. Essential as it was to furthering the science of the weather, it did have a major drawback for mariners. While used widely and to great effect, it was not as robust as many would have liked. It was not until 1844 that the French scientist Lucien Vidie (1805-1866) produced the first working aneroid barometer. This relied on the expansion or contraction of a chamber from which the air had been evacuated. His claim to be the inventor was hotly disputed in the law courts, but they finally found in his favour. He is, perhaps, underestimated, but his achievement in producing a robust instrument revolutionised the ability of ships, and later aircraft, to read pressure both for recording purposes and especially for aircraft in measuring height and hence for their own safety.

For both thermometers and barometers to have any use in weather forecasting they needed to be produced to very high standards and in large quantities. Methods of calibration as well as agreed scales were also necessary. The craftsmanship to reach the required standard progressively developed and by the beginning of the 19th century the great advances achieved meant the wide availability of accurate, robust instruments. Viewed from the 21st century, these instruments are also seen as being of great aesthetic worth.

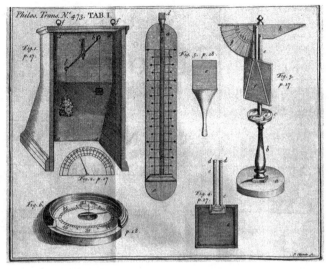

Fig 2. Set of meteorological instruments, 1744

John Dalton (1766-1844) is most famous for the great strides he made in our understanding of atomic physics. Arguably he came upon this theory somewhat by accident while studying the behaviour of atmospheric gases. Dalton's Law was formulated in 1803. He had, however, kept an astonishing record of weather observations over a period of fifty-seven years, comprising some 200,000 entries. To do this he had had to make his own instruments with which to record temperature, humidity, pressure and wind. His record appeared in his *Meteorological Essays*, first published in 1793.

We may note, in passing, some other great men who loved to keep weather records. Outstanding among these are Benjamin Franklin, Thomas Jefferson and George Washington. Few hobbies could command such illustrious devotees!

THE ENLIGHTENMENT

The period of the Enlightenment is usually taken to run from about 1650 to 1780 CE. It ushered in an amazing period of scientific progress. While some may regret the implied freedom it gave to mankind to use the earth and its resources entirely for their own benefit, it also led to a paradigm shift in philosophy as well as science. Francis Bacon (1561-1626) stands out as a key architect of the whole process. Among his best known books is *Historia Ventorum* which discusses, inter alia, air and includes probing thoughts about the nature of the atmosphere. His scientific method was based on inductive logic, demanding the meticulous gathering, testing and re-evaluation of masses of data until a substantive theory could be postulated and accepted as true: As the Royal Society put it: "… gathering comprehensive data by which we are able to recognise order in the midst of apparent confusion." The contrary view of deductive logic was that this approach was arguing from the particular to the general but this point was discounted on the assumption that enough specific information could be gathered to validate a general conclusion.

Bacon did, however, favour the idea that the moon and the planets must play an important role in fashioning the weather. As far as the distinction between science and religion was concerned he was quite clear: "Men pursue things of the present – leave the future to Divine Providence" was his philosophy. As he entered the 17th century he would have met many who saw the harsh, cold and wet years of the period portending the decline and ultimate death of the world. Men such as Robert Burton (1577-1640) in *The Anatomy of Melancholy* saw all as decay with the world "forcing all things to be bad". Bacon's scientific method was to cause much dissention, especially in the 19th century, among those seeking to forecast the weather. There were those who demanded that ever more data must be assembled before any theory could be postulated. Without some over-arching theory, forecasting was impossible. Against this group were those who took the opposite, more practical, view that attempts to develop weather forecasting must be made, for utilitarian reasons if no other, whether a law of the weather existed or not. They too called on Bacon since he believed that science should be "in the service of man's estate." A further paradox arose. Weather, like climate, was seen as different in different regions of the globe. How, then could there be a universal law of weather? These differing views helped form the tangled background to the study of the weather for the next 200 years.

A number of great men, many known in other fields, realised that air was measureable, thus advancing the science of the atmosphere, and indeed of the oceans, at this time. Robert Boyle (1627-1691), who was credited with bringing the barometer to England, and naming it, and Christopher Wren (1632-1723) have been picked out as influential, as well as Robert Hooke, to whom pride of place may justifiably be given. Hooke (1635-1703) was a true polymath; his interests covered such diverse scientific areas as anatomy, architecture, microscopy, chronometers, music, geology, optics and meteorological instruments. Furthermore, he produced instruments such as a marine barometer to further his studies. He gave his name to Hooke's law, which concerns the compression of springs. In 1663 the Royal Society asked him to set up a "method for making a history of the weather", so as to produce regular weather reports, and he designed a format for this not dissimilar to that used today. His reputation might well have been far greater but for the antipathy shown towards him by Newton, whose name carried such great weight. Hooke died all but penniless, but it is as both an experimental scientist and a designer of weather related instruments that he should be remembered.

ALMANAC AUTHORS AND WEATHER WISERS

We have already seen how early civilizations recorded the weather and tried to use astrology to describe how it worked. Astrology also appeared to provide answers in many other fields; it became the method for forecasting all manner of events, from the trivial to the momentous. By medieval times many written almanacs existed but it was in 1457 that the first one was published by Gutenberg. Surprisingly, perhaps, this was almost the same time as the first printed bible. By 1775 about 400,000 almanacs were produced in the United Kingdom each year. A major boost was given to the almanac industry when, in 1838, the tax imposed on it was abolished. Sales in that year rose to 517,000. It was said that every household contained at least two books, the Bible and an Almanac. Some, for example Old Moore's Almanac, are still on sale today. Yet all this time there were many who questioned not only the religious propriety of attempts to forecast the weather but also the need for any involvement on the part of science. Why go to all this trouble when there existed a fund of wisdom held by those whose livelihoods, and lives, depended on their accumulated experience?

These were the Weather Wisers. Their combined knowledge was best found in *The Shepherd of Banbury's Rules to Judge of the Changes in the Weather*, a volume which was published from 1670 through to 1744 and achieved a wide circulation with a detailed commentary produced as late as 1820. The rules, and there was a wide range of them, contained saws and sayings covering the immediate weather, but also some very long-range predictions. "If small clouds increase – much rain" is hardly profound while "Observe that in eight years' time there is as much south west wind as north east and consequently as many wet years as dry" is hardly intelligible. Yet, in total, they reflected the very large proportion of the population whose lives were intimately involved with the weather. Some sayings remain widely known today. Ask any group to quote one weather saying and almost all will offer: "Red sky at night shepherds' delight; red in the morning shepherds' warning". In fact this is sound science, based on the way that light is scattered. If we see red – not pink – clouds in the east they will have passed us by and give promise of fine weather the next day. Just who the Shepherd was has never been established, and some of the rules as quoted above are convoluted in the extreme. Nevertheless, the influence of the book lay more in the implication that all any forecaster needed to do was to keep a copy of the *Rules* to hand. Thus their importance, and that of many similar volumes, cannot be questioned.

Weather wisdom among seafarers was of a rather different order. Many of the sayings beaten into young midshipmen were, and are, perfectly sound and will have saved many lives at sea. They tended to be related to the immediate imperatives of ship handling, but they were born of life and death experiences. "Mare's tails and mackerel scales make tall ships carry small sails" is related to the cloud formations of cirrus and altostratus, which build ahead of a warm front and its associated bad weather. Of barometric readings, "Rise after low, expect strong blow" concerns the period just after the passage of the centre of a depression when, following a lull, wind speeds will pick up again – and blow from the opposite direction. These are but two examples of this accurate form of short term forecasting. They are discussed further in the section concerning Admiral FitzRoy, the first Head of what is now called the Met Office and sometimes described, inadequately, as the man who sailed Darwin round the world.

RECORDING THE WIND

The instruments produced by Galileo and Toricelli opened the way to the scientific recording of the weather. Yet one crucial element remained stubbornly elusive.

That was the wind: How was its speed to be measured?

Admiral Francis Beaufort (1774-1857) played a significant role in tackling this problem. Growing up in Ireland, he learnt about surveying when working with his brother. He then joined the East India Company as a midshipman. He transferred to the Royal Navy where his skill, both as a seaman and, more importantly, as a surveyor, enabled him to rise rapidly through the ranks. In 1800 he completed a survey of the coast of southern Turkey. He wrote up this voyage in a book called *Karamania*, a place name used by Europeans, but not local people. It was tellingly subtitled "A Survey of the South East Coast of Asia Minor and of the Remains of Antiquity"; naval captains were assumed to have a very wide range of skills and knowledge – including archaeology! The book remains a reference work to this day. His life at sea was ended prematurely when he was wounded in a brisk action with pirates in the Western Mediterranean. However, though shore-bound, he was retained in the Royal Navy, which was unusual and says much about the impression he had created. In 1829 he became Hydrographer to the Navy, responsible for all surveying work. He is best known for the Beaufort Wind Scale. The great advantage of his method was that it was universal and required no instruments. It was not entirely original; early Arab navigators almost certainly used some form of scale. Daniel Defoe wrote his book *The Storm* after the Great Storm of 1703; in it he bemoans the lack of any way of measuring wind speed and offers a twelve point scale, calling it his *Table of Degrees*. The Palatine Meteorological Society also proposed a scale, broken down into very small subdivisions, in the late 18th century. Both Defoe's book *The Storm* and the Palatine Meteorological Society are mentioned again later. But Beaufort standardised assessments in a way other schemes had failed to do. His table measured wind strength relative to the impact it had on a specific type of sailing ship, the frigate. It ranges from: "1 Light Air. Just sufficient wind to give steerage way" to "12 Hurricane. Wind which no canvas sail can withstand". The whole scale, as written in his diary, is shown in Fig 3. He first drafted the scale in 1806, but it was not published until 1832. In 1838 its use became compulsory in the Royal Navy, a remarkably short time for such a conservative service. In 1906 it was revised for use on land using some commonplace events such as smoke rising vertically, paper being blown along and whole branches of trees being in motion.

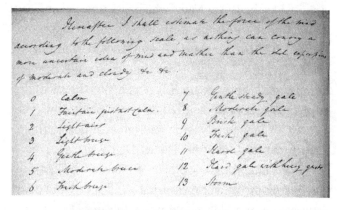

Fig 3. Beaufort wind scale, from his diary, 1806

Observing wind direction was not a problem. Most churches boasted a wind vane stemming, so the story goes, from the time when the Vatican required cockerels to be displayed on all churches, recalling St Peter's betrayal of Jesus, and these rapidly came to serve as wind vanes. At sea it was standard practice to log wind direction against the compass rose. The absence of anemometers for measuring wind speed is, however, somewhat surprising. A primitive swing plate version had been made as early as 1450. A. F. Osler (1808-1903) designed a pressure plate system that included an ingenious recording device and the polymath William Whewell (1794-1866) also produced a swing plate instrument. In 1845 Thomas Robinson (1792-1882), from the Armagh Observatory, patented a four cup instrument, which appeared promising and was not dissimilar to those we often see today. However, he assumed that its accuracy was independent of the size of the cups and the length of the arms connecting the cups to the shaft. This was not so and, as a result, the usefulness of the instrument was frequently challenged. A variety of minor improvements were made, but we had to wait until after the turn of the century for reliable anemometers to be available. The man who made this happen was William Dines (1855-1927).

Dines' father was a builder of some standing; he advised Queen Victoria about the construction of Osborne House on the Isle of Wight. He was also a keen amateur meteorologist. William was a natural mathematician, who spent time in his school holidays helping his father with tabulating rainfall data in London.

William then completed a four-year apprenticeship at a railway depot where his technical drawing skills laid a firm foundation for instrument design. To complete an all-round education that would be the envy of many, he then went up to Cambridge to study mathematics. The collapse of the Tay Bridge in Scotland in a storm in 1879 and the consequent loss of life highlighted the limited understanding that existed on the effect of wind on any standing structure. It also highlighted the lack of an accurate method of assessing wind speeds. There was, according to the eminent German climatologist Wladimir Koppen (1846-1940), "extraordinary confusion" about ways of measuring this most basic of weather features. In 1885 the Met Office set up a Wind Force Committee with Dines an active member. Over the next seventeen years he progressively perfected the design of a pressure tube anemometer (PTA). This consisted of a tube pointing directly into the wind and another open to the air, but not subject to wind pressure. A comparison of the two pressures gave a reading of wind speed. Disputes arose regularly during this period about the accuracy of the various instruments available with strong support continuing for the Robinson rotating cup version. Trials were however, to show the Dines' PTA to be clearly superior to all the rest.

By 1900 Dines was financially independent. At this time he was elected President of the Royal Meteorological Society, but governmental interest in meteorology was at a very low ebb. Work was being done across Europe and in the United States concerning the upper atmosphere, but not in the United Kingdom. Dines took up the challenge.

Meteographs existed that recorded temperature, pressure and wind at varying heights. They were attached to balloons that expanded as they rose into thinner air and eventually burst. The meteograph then fell to earth. The Met Office offered a five-shilling reward (now well over £50) for their return. Dines also used kites to lift the meteographs. He carried out a number of experiments, some less successful than others. Undaunted, he refined the equipment and the kites and arranged for them to be towed behind ships to ensure sufficient height, up to 15,000 feet, to be achieved. His meteographs became smaller and smaller, one weighed about two ounces and was little larger than a postage stamp; it required a microscope to read it. As well as his interest in the wind and the upper air, he was involved in the area his father had found of such interest: rainfall measurement. Dines truly falls into the category of a gifted amateur.

This long history of trying to measure something as basic as wind speed underlines the value of Beaufort's scale, which is still used today. But Beaufort's part in the story of meteorology is far greater than just his scale. He served for over twenty-five years as the Naval Hydrographer and his attempts to resign from the post due to his age were turned down, in part because this coincided with the outbreak, in 1854, of the Crimean War between Russia and England, France and Sardinia, of which more later. His skills in chart preparation were seen to be second to none. Throughout the first half of the 19th century his influence permeated the whole area of both surveying and of the accurate recording of weather information. His advice was also regularly sought on a wide range of topics where impartiality was important. Just one example was the Boundary Commission for redefining Parliamentary constituencies. For many of these tasks the links to the weather were not so much tenuous as non-existent.

4. FORECASTING THEORIES

Concept of a Law of Weather – Competing theories

In the late 18th and the first half of the 19th century there was a degree of certainty that there was indeed an overarching law, or series of laws, which would explain the weather. This, it was confidently held by many scientists, could lead to an assured way of predicting future weather patterns and so moving from pure science to the utilitarian value of weather forecasting. That role of pure science, to provide a constant enlargement of our knowledge of the world and how it worked, had a very good track record. Huge advances had been made and the example of astronomy showed that precise rules were there to be uncovered. Optimism was therefore the order of the day. We may note that this was a period when the concept of all embracing laws such as those found in astronomy, was much in vogue.

The comparison that was thus often made between meteorology and astronomy was not, in fact, truly valid. Much of astronomy deals with a linear problem of cause and effect. Gravity is the dominant feature enabling precise prediction of eclipses, transits and also the tides.

Thus Captain Cook could be sent to Tahiti in the certain knowledge that he would be able to observe the transit of Venus in 1769. It was such measurements that, for some, proved that meteorology could follow astronomy if only the right laws could be found. But meteorology is essentially dealing with non-linear phenomena, there are many variables and none dominate the science. In addition, astronomy had not, and has not, reached a stage where we can forecast events such as sun spot activity or the time and position of the next visible supernova explosion. When we can do these things a valid comparison between weather and astronomy can be made.

As people were casting about to understand what drove the weather, a number of theories began to emerge. If the moon caused the tides, as it clearly did, then it may well also drive the "ocean of air" immediately above the earth. Thus was born the concept of Lunar Atmospheric Tides. Luke Howard, whose achievements are discussed in the next chapter, supported this concept. Equally, it could be argued that the sun also exerted some gravitational effect, with due allowance made for the impact of the other planets in the solar system. So perhaps an astro-meteorological approach using the idea of Lunisolar Gravitational Influences would prove to hold the answer. Furthermore, the "Lunarists" (not to be confused with the Lunar Society, a group of natural philosophers who met whenever there was a full moon), held that various conjunctions of the earth and the moon could give warning of oncoming bad weather. Such ideas were welcomed by the almanac fraternity since they were essentially in line with astrological concepts – and they were easy to comprehend. Some well-known names favoured these lunar-solar theories, but some, such as Pierre-Simon Laplace (1749-1827), while initially drawn in this direction, suggested that solar heating rather than solar gravity was the more likely cause of weather patterns. We know this to be much closer to the truth, but the ways in which the other ideas were developed proved to be blind alleys. Even so, there was continuing certainty that a Law of the Weather was there to be found. Admiral FitzRoy included a chapter in his *Weather Book* explaining the lunar-solar theories. This can be seen as part of his quest to be recognised as a great scientist. He sent a copy to John Herschel (1792-1871), the renowned astronomer, and a man he much admired, only for Herschel to reject the idea out of hand.

Nor was this broad approach the only candidate for an overall theory of weather. So-called electric weather was favoured by some. This applied especially to rainfall. Water droplets, it was suggested, were in suspension due to the coatings of electricity they attract. As they rose, they cooled and their capacity to retain the charge also reduced until it was discharged by proximity to trees or buildings when the droplets would sink to the ground in the form of rain. The electric theory owed much to the work of Benjamin Franklin (1706-1790) who had brought to the fore the idea of the importance of electric phenomena with his experiments with kites flying in thunderstorms. This was a concept much espoused by G A Rowell (1804-1890), who extended, and distorted, this line of thought to explain the formation of hail as well as the presence of the aurora borealis. Rowell's progressively more plaintive appeals to people to see that he must be right fell on deaf ears and was finally swept away, as we will see, by the insights of the Bergen School.

Finally, there was the question of magnetic variation. Variation measures the difference between true north, as shown on a map, and magnetic north, which is the direction taken up by a compass needle, aligning itself with the earth's magnetic field lines. Variation loomed large for merchant and navy vessels alike since compass errors would occur unless they were adjusted at regular intervals to allow for local anomalies in the earth's magnetic field. Much effort thus went into recording magnetic values on a worldwide basis. Some saw a link between magnetic variation and storms. William Reid, who we meet below, was one of these. He suggested that "the force and frequency of storms may have some connection with the law of magnetic intensity". It may be harsh to suggest that there was thus much clutching at straws but, to mix metaphors, the field of runners for the race to the Law of Weather was large indeed.

5. THE NAMIMG OF CLOUDS

The story of cloud classification –
Impact on the arts – Howard's other achievements

The 17th and 18th centuries ushered in a period of exploration that revealed the wealth of undreamt of species of flora and fauna from across the world. Various methods of classifying this material developed, but it was not until Carl Linnaeus introduced his all-embracing system for giving a binomial name to every single plant and animal in the mid-18th century that some order was brought to this activity. From then on his taxonomy was seen as a *sine qua non* for understanding the natural world, all of which could and should be placed into precise pigeonholes. Clouds, of course, were an exception to this rule – or so it was thought. They were ever-changing in shape and movement, both horizontally and vertically. They were "the visible part of an invisible atmosphere". It took a man of rare insight to question this approach. That man was Luke Howard (1772-1864). Howard's first interest was in botany, but he was also a keen amateur meteorologist who owned two chemical works in London. He walked regularly between the two, observing and drawing the sky and he concluded that a form of classification was possible.

Fig 4. Luke Howard

He made the all-important differentiation between shapes, of which there were many, and forms, which were few in number. In essence he saw clouds as either layered, heaped or wispy. They grew and changed, covering part or all of the sky. As was the custom, he gave them Latin names – stratus, cumulus, cirrus and nimbus. Further, he made the major step of noting that they existed at different heights, and this before ballooning was past its infancy and clearly well before manned flight. He specified nine main types of cloud in his first paper entitled *"Essay on the Modification of Clouds"* which was published in 1803. His system was not, in fact, the first. Jean-Baptiste Lamarck (1744-1829) had produced something similar shortly before Howard but it is possible that his use of French names did not find favour with the scientific community. Howard's classifications were finally agreed at an international conference in 1896 and remain virtually unchanged today though each has seen the addition of many subdivisions.

The impact of Howard's work was felt not just among scientists; John Constable, the great landscape artist, was much influenced by him insisting that, "We see nothing truly until we understand it". Constable spent a considerable time on Hampstead Heath sketching innumerable cloudscapes, "skying" as he called it, so he could paint realistic landscapes with light and shade as we might see them. John Ruskin (1819-1900), the philosopher agreed. He added the thought that solitary thinkers may have solved scientific problems in the past, but that the weather was a global occurrence and that understanding demanded a combined, international effort. Johan von Goethe (1749-1832) was also among Howard's admirers and wrote a lengthy ode '*In Honour of Howard*'. And Percy Bysshe Shelley penned his poem '*The Cloud*' in 1820 in the light of the classifications. Describing the cumulonimbus he wrote:

> "I wield the flail of the lashing hail
> And whiten the green plains under
> And then again I dissolve it in rain
> And laugh as I pass in thunder."

Howard did not rest on his laurels. He turned his attention to the local climate of London. At this time London, measured by population, was the largest city in the world. Its many factories produced a great deal of heat. Not only that, Howard reasoned, the people themselves were part of the equation. The extent of domestic coal fires added hugely to both heat and pollution. In his book of 1820 called *The Climate of London*, he was describing what would now be called an urban heat island. He recorded his findings in intricate diagrams; their circular pattern balanced times of year against temperature anomalies with a quotation from Virgil at the centre. Perhaps for artistic effect, the signs of the zodiac run around the circumference. It was pioneering work, even if it took over a hundred years before the Great London Smog of 1952 triggered the Clean Air Act of 1956 to bring some relief to the Capital and the country.

6. THE LIGHTER THAN AIR BRIGADE

Ballooning – Glaisher's great escape –
The use of kites – Airships

Ballooning came to the fore towards the end of the 18th century with the first lift-off by a hydrogen-filled balloon taking place in 1783. James Sadler (1753-1828) was the first Englishman to make an ascent, taking off from Oxford in November 1784. At almost the same time a hot air balloon flew, first with animals and then, in November, with humans on board. This was under the direction of the Montgolfier brothers and it is in honour of them that, in French, a balloon is called a montgolfier. A flight from Dover to Calais followed in 1785.

We mention later the work of George Airy (1801-1892), the Astronomer Royal. One of his protégé's in meteorological matters was James Glaisher (1809-1903). Glaisher is probably best remembered for his ballooning exploits, described below, but his earlier days are also relevant. A bright young man, he moved to the observatory at Greenwich in 1835 initially to help with work on magnetism. His father had been an instrument maker and James inherited his father's demand for precision. Then, under Airy's direction, he set up some sixty weather observation sites across the country, staffed mainly by clergy and doctors. The extensive railway system, as well as the telegraph, was used to pass the information they gathered to Glaisher. The aim was data collection, pure and simple, certainly not for carrying out forecasting. Glaisher was something of an autocrat – but he also had an eye for business. Some of the reports that he generated at his work he then sold to the newspapers and also at the Great Exhibition in 1851 at the cost of 1d. He was not above putting his name to these reports, though they were hardly all his own work. Nor was he averse to using information from both Greenwich and from Kew where he also worked and where all instruments were calibrated. Some in scientific societies looked down on him considering him something of a tradesman. Yet he must have been a powerful personality for he kept his feet in both scientific camps, that is the Royal Society and its rival the British Society for the Advancement of Science which had been set up expressly because of the reactionary approach of the Royal Society. The system for collecting data called for considerable organisational skills and a willingness to use the latest, telegraph, technology. The assembled records did have potential value in building up a picture of the climate. Yet reading in the *Daily News* what weather had occurred the day before yesterday may have been of passing interest, but it hardly advanced scientific knowledge. It certainly did not usher in an era of weather forecasting. Where his observational skills came to the fore was in his meticulous studies of the formation of dew and the composition of ice crystals. Yet for all his dedication no new scientific advances stemmed from hours of study. Glaisher has been called Britain's first weather forecaster but this is to overstate his efforts, which were essentially to collect and publish observations. Nevertheless, he was a polymath with a prodigious work output. He described himself with some accuracy as "an engine with a thousand wheels".

Glaisher is still probably best known as a balloonist. Ballooning had become a popular pastime by the middle of the century. Adventure flights, for those who could afford them, were frequently undertaken. By 1852 Charles Green (1785-1870) had completed many flights, mainly using coal gas. His 500th took place in September of that year with eight passengers and ended at 10pm on Pirbright Green in North West Surrey. Astonished locals appeared "out of nowhere" and, initially fearful, were finally persuaded to help tether the balloon. The landing was recorded in the *Illustrated London News* complete with a dramatic woodcut.

Little use had been made of any of these flights to study the upper atmosphere. By 1859 a decision had been made to try and rectify this situation. A Balloon Committee was formed by the British Association for the Advancement of Science, and Glaisher was invited to act as observer and recorder on a series of ascents. Coal gas was usually used as a cheaper option to hydrogen, so gas plants became the meeting place for interested spectators. One flight particularly captured the public's imagination. Together with Henry Coxwell (1819-

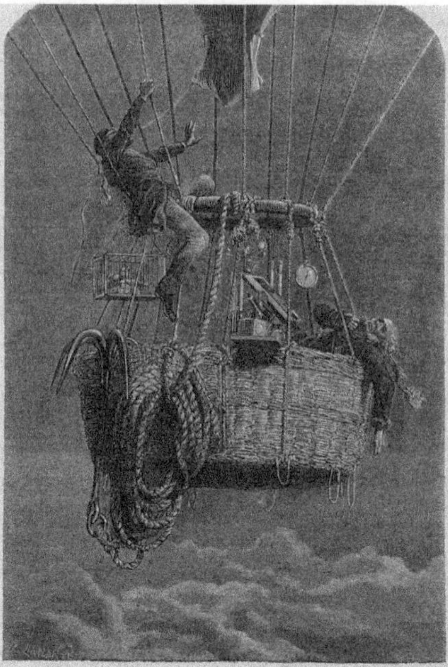

"AERIAL VOYAGES."

ously hauling in the rope, until each was brought safely alongside, and got into the boat, which, with God's blessing, they all reached in safety. No time was then lost in getting them on board the steamer, where they enjoyed the warmth of the engine-room; and the little vessel made the best of her way to Penzance, followed by the hearty cheers of the party on the rock.

Christmas Day, associated with "the glad tidings of great joy" and with many happy and holy thoughts, seems a fitting occasion for the consummation of such a good work; and its completion has enabled the Elder Brethren of the Trinity House to carry out their earnest desire of offering, as their New-Year's gift, a blessing to

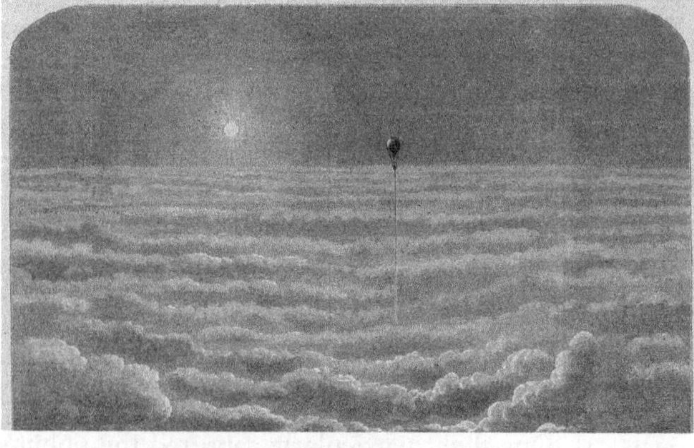

Fig 5. Pages from the *Illustrated London News* describing James Glaisher's ballooning exploits

1900), an experienced balloonist, Glaisher was caught in severe updraughts and reached a height estimated to be about 35,000 feet. He passed out and Coxwell, whose hands were frozen, only saved the day by pulling on the chord to vent gas with his teeth. Coxwell roused Glaisher by insisting he continued with his observations, which Glaisher did with the same precision that he had exercised on the ascent! Dramatic pictures appeared in the *London Illustrated News* (see Fig 5.), another example of this influential magazine's skill at entertaining its wide readership. This particular ascent rather overshadowed the continuing work of studying the upper air; a total of twenty-eight ascents were completed. Important data was gathered showing that temperature could increase as well as decrease with increases in altitude. Without knowing it, Glaisher's acute observations, often written in poetic language, foreshadowed the idea of a jet stream, "a Gulf Stream of air" as he called it.

Ballooning in the United States had a mainly military role, though mail was first carried in a balloon in 1793. Later, much research was carried out by Professor A L Rotch (1861-1912) of the Blue Hills Observatory; he recorded the highest balloon ascent in the United States and proposed the use of kites flown from ships to study the upper atmosphere over the sea. He also noted that air temperatures could rise with height in cumulus clouds. This idea was scornfully dismissed by some in the scientific establishment as late as the early 1900s, even though Glaisher had earlier noted the same effect.

We have seen something of the adventures of Glaisher, but many other balloonists became involved through into the next the century. In 1901 Arthur Berson (1859-1942), a German balloonist, made an ascent to 34,500 feet – it may have been 35,500 feet, but the ink froze in the barograph carried aboard the balloon – and he just survived the experience. He was also instrumental in attempting to arrange simultaneous ascents from a number of locations in Europe to obtain a synchronous upper air plot over as wide an area as possible. Leon Teisserenc de Bort (1855-1913) was another major player; he made over 200 ascents using hydrogen filled balloons and is credited with "discovering", in 1902, the tropopause, the dividing line between the troposphere and stratosphere, which occurs at between 30,000 feet and 35,000 feet, as seen by Teisserenc de Bort, though we now know it can be as high as 56,000 feet dependent on latitude.

Kites also played an important part in this study of the upper atmosphere. We have already mentioned the work of William Dines and A L Rotch. Lawrence Hargrave (1850-1915), from Scotland used box kites and William Eddy (1850-1909) in the United States tried a Malay variety. Trains of box kites were used, joined together with piano wire, which was payed out under the control of a steam engine with 10,000 feet regularly being reached. There was sufficient activity in this area for tables of results to be regularly published in the *Met Office Journal*. That of 1913 recorded a range of figures to a height of over 10,000 feet. Kites similar to those of Hargrave and Eddy are still in use in the Antarctic today.

As well as balloons and kites, airships had a role to play in the field of meteorology and it is appropriate to carry the narrative forward to cover their story. Their great size made them vulnerable to weather conditions and especially to the wind. They were also susceptible to lightning strikes. They were slow, but, even by today's standards, had great endurance. This put extra demands on the need for longer-range weather forecasts over extended distances. In 1884 the airship *La France* covered eight kilometres in twenty-three minutes. This flight greatly influenced Count von Zeppelin (1838-1917), who built a number of airships and, from 1900 to the start of the First World War gave flights to over one thousand passengers. This success with Zeppelins may have led to overconfidence on the part of the German High Command in the First World War. Military Zeppelins were required to fly as high as 10,000 feet to avoid the possibility of attack by fighter aircraft, but there were no means of predicting, as against measuring, winds at such heights. As a result losses of German airships were considerable; on one raid five out of eleven machines were lost over France, having been blown miles off track.

After the First World War the United Kingdom followed other European powers in building airships, with a number completing trans-Atlantic flights. The airship was seen by many in the United Kingdom as the ideal vehicle for flying to and from the outposts of the Empire and the trans-Atlantic flight of the R34 in 1919 gave support to this view. So, in 1929, the R100 and R101 were built to prove this concept. Significantly, the ability to carry 200 troops formed part of the specification. Extensive modifications were needed to both of them before they could be ready to undertake the task. This entailed cutting them in half and fitting a large new centre section to improve buoyancy. The two machines were built by different manufacturers and the story of the secrecy and competition between them is not an edifying one; nor is the role of politicians and diplomats who had set a timetable for a first flight to India and were reluctant to see it slip. R101 undertook very limited flight-testing after modification and that in almost perfect weather, but still took off on schedule in October 1930. The weather conditions, unsurprisingly for that time of year, were far from ideal. Sadly R101 crashed in turbulent weather close to the Beauvais Ridge in Northern France. There were few survivors and those who lost their lives included the Air Minister, Lord Thomson. This accident spelled the end of British airship flights, just as the lightning strike, which destroyed the Hindenburg Zeppelin in New Jersey in 1937, did for the Germans. Airships were subsequently used by the Americans in the anti-submarine role, but this was quite short-lived. So airships can be seen more as victims of the weather rather than vehicles that helped with the understanding of weather phenomena. Perhaps this underlined what sailors had long known: the weather can be a powerful servant but a destructive master.

7. THE TELEGRAPH AND WEATHER CHARTS

The telegraphic revolution – Weather charts – Palatine Meteorological Society – Which way does the wind blow? – Synoptic charts – Inclusion of medical details

We are used to marvelling at the communications revolution that has taken place around the turn of the 21st century. We note the impact it has had on so many aspects of everyday living. In exactly the same way, it is difficult to over-estimate the impact that the introduction of the telegraph had on a worldwide basis in the 1830s; virtually instant, two-way communications were possible. At the same time railway systems were spreading rapidly, facilitating the expansion of the telegraph network. All these developments forced countries to introduce standard time zones. Quite apart from the imperative of the railway timetable, these were, of course, crucial if simultaneous weather observations were to be made. In 1847 the Railway Clearing House in the United Kingdom introduced a common time, but it was not until 1880 that Greenwich Mean Time was legally adopted throughout the British Isles. In the United States, with its extensive east-west longitude, the requirement was even more pressing. In 1879 there were over 100 official time zones and Cleveland Abbe (1838-1916), the meteorologist, proposed that there should be just four. This would greatly facilitate the recording of weather information and eventually the current five zones were agreed in 1883. Germany introduced a standard time in 1893. France continued to use Paris Mean Time until 1911.

The telegraph needed a simple code for its messages to be effective and Samuel Morse provided this in 1837. He had many obstacles to overcome before his dots and dashes became the established mode of using telegraphy. It was not until 1843 that the transmission of the message "What God hath Wrought" between Baltimore and Washington convinced the United States authorities that here was not just a viable but also amazingly useful system.

By 1850 there was a cable across the English Channel and shortly after the start of the Crimean War, there were reliable links all the way from Balaclava to London. Less than twenty years later the first successful trans-Atlantic cable had been laid. Radiotelephony was still many years away; the first successful transmission did not take place until 1906.

Apart from the requirement for a standard time, it was the speed with which weather information could be transmitted that completely changed the picture. The problem of receiving data quickly and simultaneously from observers in many locations was overcome and forecasters were then able to build up a synchronous picture of weather patterns over a wide area. That, in turn, opened the door for the transmission of warnings back to the observers when extreme weather situations were recognised and seen as significant. Thus the telegraph may be seen as the *sine qua non* of timely weather warning systems.

This shift in perception did not immediately register with the more reactionary elements of the scientific community. We will see that the fallout from the international conference of 1853 on sharing weather information to support trade, triggered moves in Holland, France, the United States and the United Kingdom to at least look to the possibility of issuing storm warnings. These became dear to the hearts of the mariners but anathema to some commercial interests who feared that false warnings would dent profit margins. There were also those who questioned the validity of any predictions, which were not based on what they saw as a sound scientific foundation. We see more of these tensions later on.

WEATHER CHARTS

The desire to produce maps and charts stretches back to the earliest days of civilization. Yet these dealt with static situations; coastlines did not alter, at least in the short term, and mountains only moved imperceptibly. By the 16th and 17th centuries the work of cartographers had refined this process so that local and global maps were commonplace if not entirely accurate. Much of this work centred on showing ownership of land, be it a manorial estate or the boundaries of a nation. But no one owned the atmosphere. Thus the idea of mapping something as changeable as the weather was no more than a distant dream. It was not until the late 18th century that this situation began to change. An early map is from Northern France. It shows the path of a massive storm of 1788 which brought with it devastating hailstones. These cut swathes through the fields where crops were about to be harvested, robbing peasant farmers of their livelihoods. Some historians suggest that this storm, in combination with others, paved the way to the Bastille and the guillotine.

A more helpful start point for consideration of the development of the charts that are now so familiar is the epidemics that struck many parts of Europe in the late 1700s. The epidemics were virulent and it was believed at the time that there was some link between air quality and weather conditions in general. Miasma, or night air, was thought to cause the transmission of diseases such as cholera, and were seen to be linked directly to atmospheric pressure. As a result a medico-meteorological network was set up to gather pressure information. This was the Palatine Meteorological Society founded by the Elector of Mannheim, Carl Theodore, in 1780. He, perhaps, had rather more interest in meteorology than in medicine. The Society collected pressure readings from right across Europe, from Norway to Rome and England to St Petersburg. It continued this work until 1795. The mass of accumulated data provided little indication of any link between atmospheric pressure and health. It lay unnoticed until Heinrich Brandes (1777-1834) came across it. Brandes was a water engineer whose main preoccupation was the state of the banks of the River Weser. He then became a professor of mathematics.

When he looked at the data, he was appalled by the endless columns of figures and started to plot them out onto charts. By 1820 he had completed the mammoth task of drawing a chart showing pressure readings for every day of the year 1783. He said of his work: "If one could collect more precise reports of the weather, even if only for the whole of Europe, it would surely yield very instructive results". He clearly grasped the global nature of the weather. However, he also drew the conclusion that the wind blew from the periphery of storms into their centre rather than flowing around them. His assertion clouded this particular issue for many years to come.

Brandes' efforts were noted by a number of highly respected scientists. Their belief was that a way of forecasting the weather with a high degree of certainty would be found in the near future; it was just a question of time. Among those supporting this view was George Airy who was appointed Astronomer Royal in 1835, a position he held until 1881. He agreed the view that prediction was the primary purpose of studying weather and told the British Association for the Advancement of Science that meteorology was a "desperate" science but could have value as a matter of practical use. The influential John Ruskin, as we saw above, also agreed with this view.

WHICH WAY DOES THE WIND BLOW?

But, throughout this period, the support Brandes had given to the idea that the wind blew in towards the centre of a depression, continued to cause controversy.

We will follow this story through to its resolution. Elias Loomis (1811-1889), the son of a Baptist minister, was an American professor of mathematics and he became involved in the debate. His interest was awakened by a particularly violent storm that struck the eastern coast of the United States in February 1838. He plotted isobars, isallobars (lines joining places of equal pressure change), isothermal lines and included wind vector arrows very similar to those currently in use. Yet analysis of the storm raised many questions concerning its forward speed, direction of movement and the behaviour of the wind around it. The Loomis chart did not resolve the issue about whether wind blew round storms or into their centre from all directions in part because of the paucity of observations. But it did show the huge value a chart has over endless columns of numbers. "A set of maps for the whole of the United States for a year would settle the question of the laws of storms", stated Loomis. We shall hear more of him later on.

This central question of wind movement around extra-tropical storms brought two men in the United States into acrimonious conflict. One was James Espy (1785-1860) who became a full time meteorologist in Philadelphia in 1830. Espy, in contrast to Loomis, produced masses of data over the period 1842 to 1854, but much of this was contained in lists without the aid of charts. Loomis was scathing about the lack of graphic presentation exhibited by Espy who did then produce charts for the period 1851-1852. These, however, failed to show any centres of low pressure. They certainly did not resolve the issue about wind circulation. Espy stuck with his view that Brandes was correct and demonstrated, at least to his own satisfaction, that air was drawn directly into the centre of depressions. His views were seriously challenged by William Redfield (1789-1857), who owned a fleet of steamers. He was an amateur meteorologist with a passion for accurate weather observations which he recorded as his steamers plied their trade on the eastern seaboard of the United States. In 1831 he published his findings; that the wind blew anti-clockwise around depressions in the northern hemisphere. Thus Espy met him head on. Espy was not one to admit he might be wrong, especially when his opponent was merely the untrained owner of a few steamships. An unpleasant, public dispute followed and simmered for some years.

During this period Redfield found a useful ally. William Reid (1791-1858) was a British army engineer and in 1832 he was sent to Barbados to help with the reconstruction on the Island following a devastating hurricane. While there he became fascinated by the storm that had caused his visit. He had no particular axe to grind; he simply wanted to understand why the storm had been so damaging. As well as supervising the rebuilding work he gathered as much data about the hurricane as he could. He was puzzled by the contrast between the strength of the winds and the slow progress of the storm over the ground. In addition, the wind directions recorded near the storm appeared to shift round the compass at an alarming rate. He found time to travel to nearby islands and diligently amassed an impressive set of charts showing the passage of the storm. There was no answer other than that the winds were "rotary", circulating around the centre in an anti-clockwise direction. He was delighted to find that someone else shared his views – that someone was Redfield. They became close friends. Reid carried out extensive research covering the Southern Hemisphere and the Indian Ocean. He wrote up his findings in a detailed work called *An Attempt to Develop a Law of Storms by Means of Facts*; the title is apt since the book contains a mass of detail, especially from ships' logs; these were the facts. It did much to win over the European establishment to the rotary concept. Reid's painstaking research seldom gets the credit it deserves. He showed that tropical cyclones formed in latitudes between 10 and 30 degrees and noted that greater damage was done by storm surges than by high winds. His examination of ships' logs highlights the value some captains placed on the sympiesometer to forewarn of approaching storms. This instrument used almond oil, rather than the more expensive mercury, and hydrogen that expanded and contracted as air pressure altered. While it did react more quickly to pressure changes than a conventional barometer it was less robust and the hydrogen could leak away through the oil. The advent of the aneroid barometer proved its death knell. A man given to accurate observation and recording, Reid was also an excellent administrator. He was involved in the organisation of the Great Exhibition of 1851 and went on to act as Governor in a number of colonies. His fair but firm rule led to him becoming known as The Good Governor.

In fact both camps had useful insights to offer; Redfield and Reid were clearly right about wind circulation, the major part of the controversy. Air does indeed move directly towards areas of lower pressure. However, once that air is in motion the earth's rotation (the Coriolis effect) comes into play and the air is deflected, to the right in the northern hemisphere, until it reaches a point of equilibrium when it is circulating around the periphery. Espy was right in one respect: his theory that higher temperatures, which caused the air to rise, were fundamental to the formation of storms. However, his claim that, using this information, he would be able to light a fire big enough to produce clouds and hence rain served only to undermine his already waning reputation. The way the discussion was conducted did little credit, especially to Espy, but is a reflection of the heat that can be generated during scientific disputes; perhaps one may even claim that this form of dialectic is one way scientific advances are made.

Another well known European meteorologist had an input to this matter. He was C H D Buys Ballot (1817-1890), a Dutch chemist and mathematician whose law offers an easily understood rule for locating areas of low pressure. It states that: "If you stand with your back to the wind in the northern hemisphere low pressure will be on your left". He can also lay claim to setting up the first storm warning system, which covered four stations on the coast of the Netherlands. It became operational on 1st June 1860. Strangely he did not continue to investigate the weather, though in 1873 he was appointed the first chairman of the newly formed International Meteorological Organisation. More attention to his rule, which the American William Ferrel (1817-1891) also noted, might have helped cool the fevered arguments over cyclonic circulation. Some meteorologists simply sat on the fence in this dispute; Matthew Maury (1806-1873), the leading American meteorologist, would only say the question was yet to be resolved. Heinrich Dové (1803-1879) was a Prussian climatologist and meteorologist who had also thrown his hat into the ring. Dové had as many detractors as he had admirers. Humboldt called him the father of meteorology while others suggested he "seriously retarded progress", a view supported by the climatologist Koppen. Dové certainly proved most influential with his work *The Law of Storms*, a popular title since the word law added credence to the text. It was translated into English in 1862 and described, among other things, the movement of the wind in the vicinity of low-pressure areas, which was largely in line with the ideas of Espy. The translation was completed by Robert Scott (1833-1900), who became the second head of the Met Office. Dové did help set up observation stations in the then united Germany, but these were mainly to gather climatic data. There was little interest in a national weather bureau in Germany and, as late as 1888, Bismarck would not hear of it. Yet Dové's book, though in error in this important area, remained widely read and quoted.

The full understanding of the pattern of weather around low-pressure areas continued to elude scientists well into the late 1800s. A number offered ideas, but these tended to be descriptive rather than based on any firm foundation. Ralph Abercrombie (1842-1897) was one of these. Abercrombie was well travelled and an acute observer of the weather. He wrote *Seas and Skies in Many Latitudes*, which was widely read. He was an influential man and worked in partnership with Hugo Hilderbrandsson (1838-1926), who was a member of the International Meteorological Organisation, playing a useful part in promoting Luke Howard's cloud classification at the Conference of 1896 when the final classifications were agreed. Abercrombie is also notable for his interest in photography, especially taking pictures of clouds. Both he and Hilderbrandsson were less interested in the actual names given to clouds, but rather that everyone called the same clouds by the same name. He started a tradition now splendidly reflected in organisations such as the Cloud Appreciation Society. The Society's populist title masks the importance of some of its scientific work notably in gaining acceptance of a new subcategory of cloud, asperitas. The CAS now boasts a worldwide membership of over 40,000 in over 100 countries.

Abercrombie's attempt to draw up an accurate chart of cyclonic prognostics in 1887 may cause some amusement since it depicts rapid changes in health with the passage of the low-pressure area; aches and pains, corns and smelly drains are to be found next to a watery sun and pale moon. The idea of a linkage between medicine and the weather is a narrow thread running through much of the discussion about meteorology and, in fairness, it should be pointed out that Abercrombie suffered from poor health from an early age and died aged fifty-five. However, prognostications that combined medical and meteorological terms gave regular ammunition to magazines such as *Punch* to poke fun at the scientific community. Even so we should note the wider picture of the impact of bad weather on the lives of those many people who were dependant on agriculture both to make a living and for simple survival. In 1815 a massive volcanic eruption occurred at Mount Tambora on Sumbawa in Indonesia and threw millions of tons of debris into the atmosphere, triggering the "Year without a summer" in 1816. It showed the level of vulnerability of the worldwide farming community. The 1860s and 1870s brought particularly wet summers, not just resulting in ruined harvests, but reflected in civil unrest and, many critics suggest, in much of the literature and poetry of the period, it also promoted interest in plants that flourish in damp climates. An example, close to home for the author, is the work of Fanny Tripp in her definitive work of 1868 on British mosses.

At a more popular level, there was a growing fascination throughout the second half of the 19th century with the natural world, both in the different climatic areas of the earth and of the atmosphere above them. There were great expectations about what might be discovered as well as a sense of wonder stimulated by such prolific writers as G Lartwig (1813-1880) whose book *The Aerial World* was a best seller.

8. MOVES TOWARDS STORM WARNINGS

The Crimean War – The Black Sea storm

A number of events in the 1850s added ever more urgency to the need to forecast the weather. One of these occurred on 14th November 1854 at the start of the Crimean War. Massive British and French fleets had recently arrived at Balaclava, on the edge of the Black Sea, and were in the process of unloading both personnel and stores. A major storm swept right across Europe and caused havoc on its arrival in the Black Sea. There was great loss of life and major damage among the vessels there. Thirty French and British ships were wrecked and forty seriously damaged. For the British the greatest loss was the new, sail-cum-steam transport ship *HMS Prince*; of the 150 people on board only six survived. The entire cargo was lost including 40,000 greatcoats and the same number of pairs of boots. This rocked the morale of troops settling in for a long winter campaign. For the French, the loss of the 100-gun Flagship *Henry IV* was especially significant. The storm was a rare, but by no means unique event.

The disaster followed on from a series of military debacles. The loss of much equipment through poor planning, a defeat avoided only by the heroics of the "Thin Red Line", the charge of the Light Brigade – all these raised serious doubts about the capabilities of the higher command. Questions were immediately asked as to why this further disaster could not have been avoided, especially in view of the lengthy track of the storm across Europe and the resulting long warning time that existed prior to its arrival. Furthermore, the availability of telegraph communications over virtually the whole of Europe meant warnings should surely have been issued? Not surprisingly, the military in the Crimea detested the idea of the use of the telegraph since this allowed the War Office to meddle with the day-to-day running of the campaign.

There was much wringing of hands over the incident. In France, Napoleon III ordered a major inquiry. It was headed by the astronomer and scientist Le Verrier (1811-1877) who had become famous for calculating that the planet Neptune must exist before it was actually observed. He called for readings from locations along the track of the storm from as far afield as Greenwich. In addition he started to plan a network of observers who could use the telegraph to gather weather information across Europe. This became the *Bulletin Internationale* which would help him plot the track of any storms and issue warnings accordingly. No concerns here about the niceties of understanding everything about the weather before trying to predict its future patterns! His efforts exemplify the view that attempts at forecasting were essentially born out of the need for storm warnings rather than for any other purpose. To find out more about the storm he appointed a young meteorologist, Emmanuel Liais (1826-1900), to plot out its track. Liais thought that the probable cause of the storm was a cold air mass pressing in from the north that helped form atmospheric tidal waves. He also noted various kinks in the pattern of isobars, which were linked to the storm. Le Verrier was much taken with the concept of these waves and pursued the tidal wave theory with some vigour. Unfortunately Le Verrier was a man with a very short fuse and Liais became embroiled in some of the arguments that were then bedevilling the French scientific world following the revolutions of 1848. Falling foul of Le Verrier, he went to live in Brazil. There he became a noted astronomer and has a moon crater named after him.

Thus it was that the Black Sea storm impacted on the thinking of those in positions of power in central government. The issuing of storm warnings was now, per force, on their agenda.

9. THE SPECIAL CASE OF VICE-ADMIRAL ROBERT FITZROY

*Setting up the Met Office – Conflicting requirements –
The "Golden Wreck" – Cones and Drums – The last days
– Reinstatement of the warning system*

Admiral FitzRoy (1804-1864) is often remembered, as has been said, as the man who sailed Charles Darwin round the world, but he was a central figure in the development of weather forecasting and in the issuing of weather warnings in the United Kingdom. His efforts did much to break the hold of those scientists who revolted at the idea of trying to make forecasts in the absence of any agreed law of weather. But he was also a tragic figure in the Shakespearian sense. Greatly talented, his very nature was, in part, the cause of his downfall, but his achievements deserve the more lengthy coverage given here.

Robert FitzRoy was born into the aristocracy in 1805. He was descended from the Duke of Grafton who was one of the many illegitimate children of Charles II. His grandfather was the Marquis of Londonderry; he had two uncles who were admirals and his father was a major general. Another uncle was Lord Castlereagh. So the aristocracy and the military were very much in his blood. And his name FitzRoy is an Anglicisation of Fils du Roi, son of the King.

VICE-ADMIRAL ROBERT FITZROY, C.B., F.R.S.
DIRECTOR OF THE METEOROLOGICAL OFFICE
1855-65

Fig 6. Robert FitzRoy as a young man

He was sent to the Royal Naval College at Portsmouth at the age of 12 and completed the three-year course in twenty months, graduating with the Gold Medal as the outstanding student. In 1824, he was commissioned as a lieutenant. A great deal of the Navy's work at this time was spent surveying and in 1828 FitzRoy found himself in Rio de Janeiro acting as Flag Lieutenant to Admiral Otway. The Admiral, against the advice of his staff, appointed FitzRoy Captain of *HMS Beagle* – at the age of twenty-three. The circumstances were not auspicious. The previous captain, Captain Stokes, had committed suicide, finding the stress of captaincy in the region of Tierra del Fuego, perhaps the toughest sailing waters on the globe, simply overwhelming. FitzRoy proved to be an outstanding captain and surveyor. He returned to the United Kingdom in 1830 to a hero's welcome. In 1831 *HMS Beagle* was re-commissioned and completed the remarkable round the world voyage with Charles Darwin on board mainly to check on the correctness of the recorded longitude of important locations. FitzRoy returned with eighty-two charts together with maps of eighty harbours, as well as an astonishing selection of flora, fauna and geological specimens. A great future was predicted for him.

A wide variety of appointments followed, but it was in 1854 that FitzRoy's next direct encounter with meteorological matters took place. By this time it was clear that he was a workaholic, imbued with the Victorian obsession with duty. He fervently wished to be recognised as a true scientist. As we have seen there were a variety of theories about why we had weather and, for a time, he supported the luni-solar idea as part of his effort to be the one to formalise a law of weather, and be recognised for doing so. He also had a real concern, and compassion, for ordinary sailors. The loss of life at sea at this time was horrendous; more details are given in the Annex. Some resulted from major shipwrecks, but many were caused by storms striking smaller fishing vessels, fleets of colliers and the ferries, which were widely used in many coastal areas. Small communities around the coast could be, literally, decimated by storms, even of only moderate intensity.

In 1853 there was a major international conference on the weather held in Paris, largely at the instigation of the American meteorologist Matthew Maury. Maury had joined the United States Navy with a promising career ahead of him, but suffered a serious leg injury making him unfit for sea duty. However, he published an extensive series of Wind and Ocean Current charts covering the North Atlantic. As a Virginian, he joined the Confederates during the American Civil War and spent time in Europe seeking support and supplies. After the war ended he wrote a number of influential books on a range of subjects, especially on oceanography but also including several on meteorology. The purpose of the 1853 conference was to facilitate travel at sea by recording and standardising data about winds and currents. In essence, Maury wished to see this data set out on wind charts to be universally available to all sailors. The outcome of the conference for the United Kingdom, was the setting up, in 1854, of what we now know as the Met Office. It was located within the Board of Trade with FitzRoy appointed as the Meteorological Statist to the Board of Trade. However, there was a lack of clarity about what exactly he was supposed to be doing and for whom. The Board of Trade and the Admiralty wanted data to aid with navigation at sea; shorter passage times was the goal. The scientific community, represented by the Royal Society, was closely involved and seen, especially by themselves, as the professional overseers of the office. They wanted slightly different data that could aid pure research. They were very much in the mould of Francis Bacon's scientific method of gathering data, testing it and then by inductive logic producing a scientific law. They saw FitzRoy's role essentially as gathering that data. There was also pressure from those concerned with the loss of life at sea, mentioned above. By chance that very year the Institute for the Preservation of Life at Sea from Shipwreck became the Royal National Lifeboat Institution. It was FitzRoy's task to struggle through this maze.

The newly formed office, with its very small staff, started gathering data. Ships were commissioned to transcribe information from their logs on to specially designed forms and then to send it in to the Statist for collation. By 1855 over fifty merchant ships were sending in data as well as two naval vessels and the number involved was growing rapidly. After a short interlude a steady and relentless flow of figures started to arrive. The result was the production of wind star diagrams (see Fig 7.) that showed the percentage of time the wind blew from a particular direction over a particular period of time. The format used was an improved version of that proposed by Maury, and differences about which was the better format proved to be a source of some friction between the two men. The wind stars were collated into atlases for many parts of the globe, with the diagrams normally covering a three-month period.

But FitzRoy remained horrified by the loss of life at sea. Based very much on his own experience as a sea captain, he concluded that one of the main answers lay with the proper use of the barometer. If people could see that pressure was falling, especially if that fall was rapid, then they should not set sail. He began to formulate a number of ideas. Every port should have a barometer and, most importantly, it should be available for everyone to see – and to understand how to interpret it. Hence there had to be instructions to go with it. This lead to the FitzRoy barometer which displayed a card behind the column of mercury with useful advice about the significance of rising and falling pressure. FitzRoy insisted that what was offered was essentially advisory; the final decision on whether or not to sail must lie with the ship's captain.

In addition, if people with barometers and thermometers sent in their readings, all taken at the same time, these could be plotted onto a synoptic chart. The term synoptic chart was coined by FitzRoy and is indicative of his deep Christian feelings. He based the idea on the three synoptic gospels which taken together, were seen as representing the whole picture of Jesus' life. The charts could be used to forecast areas where there might be storms. It would then be possible to issue warnings to the relevant ports of the weather they might expect. The means for all this communication was available. It was the telegraph.

414

SQUARE 375.

Subdivided into *a, b, c, d*, which subdivision may be continued by quartering and lettering *a, b, c, d*, as *e, f, g, h*, &c.

SOUTH ATLANTIC.

Brazilian Coast (near Rio de Janeiro).
For Three Months — January, February, March.

Four Windroses are condensed into this Diagram; namely, those for—

	a	*b*	*c*	*d*
Lats. and	20°+25° S.	20°+25° S.	25°+30° S.	25°+30° S.
Longs.	30°+35° W.	35°+40° W.	30°+35° W.	35°+40° W.

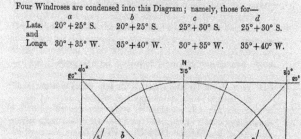

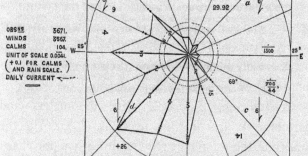

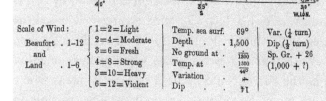

Fig 7. Wind star diagram for the South Atlantic for January, February and March showing the prevailing wind from the South and South West together with a wide range of other information

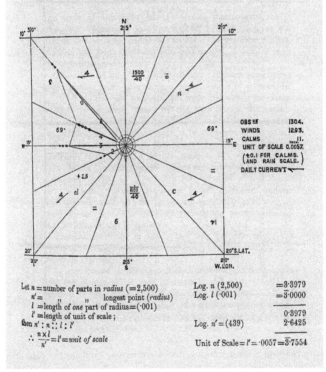

PRINCIPLES OF WIND STARS   415

SQUARE 338.

SOUTH ATLANTIC.
Brazilian Coast (near Bahia).
For Three Months — January, February, March.

Five-inch Square : half one side (=radius of inscribed circle) has 2,500-thousandths of an inch, in which measure the *unit for scale* is taken.

Let n = number of parts in *radius* (=2,500)
n' = ,, ,, ,, longest point (*radius*)
l = length of *one* part of radius = (·001)
l' = length of unit of scale ;
then $n' : n :: l : l'$
∴ $\dfrac{n \times l}{n'} = l'$ = *unit of scale*

Log. n (2,500) = 3·3979
Log. l (·001) = $\overline{3}$·0000

0·3979
Log. $n' = (439)$ = 2·6425

Unit of Scale = $l' = $ ·0057 = $\overline{3}$·7554

Fig 7. Wind star diagram for another part of the South Atlantic for January, February and March showing the prevailing wind from the North West and West.

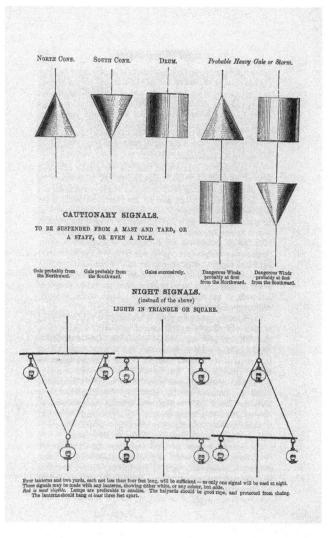

Fig 8. Diagram of storm warning cones and drums for both day and night use

351

WEATHER REPORT, 1862.

28th July 8 A.M. Monday.	B	E	D	W	F	X	C	I	H	R	S
Nairn	29·84	55	1	SW.	5	7	1	b	2	0·23	2
Aberdeen	29·77	56	6	SW.	5	7	4	c	—	—	2
Leith	29·83	59	5	SW.	6	6	4	m	—	—	3
Berwick	30·00	54	3	SE.	4	3	4	b	—	—	1
Ardrossan	29·99	55	2	NW.	5	6	7	o	2	0·13	4
Portrush	30·03	54	2	SW.	4	1	2	b	—	—	3
Galway	30·16	56	2	Z.	0	6	2	b	—	—	1
Valentia	30·22	63	7	WNW.	1	4	2	b	—	—	4
Queenstown	30·18	58	3	NW.	1	3	1	b	—	—	1
Holyhead	30·11	57	4	WSW.	3	3	3	c	—	—	3
Liverpool	30·15	57	1	WSW.	3	3	6	c	—	—	2
Pembroke	30·18	57	4	NW.	1	2	5	b	—	—	1
Penzance	30·22	60	1	NNE.	2	4	4	c	—	—	2
Plymouth	30·17	58	5	NW.	1	5	3	b	—	—	1
Jersey	30·20	61	4	N.	3	1	4	c	—	—	2
Weymouth	30·18	61	5	WSW.	1	3	3	c	—	—	3
Portsmouth	30·16	60	5	NNE.	3	4	3	c	—	—	2
Dover	30·15	63	1	E.	2	3	1	b	—	—	1
London	30·18	57	4	NNW.	2	4	2	b	—	—	
Yarmouth	30·14	61	5	N.	2	4	1	b	—	—	1
Scarborough	30·11	57	3	W.	2	3	5	b	—	—	2
Shields	30·07	55	5	W.	4	4	5	o	—	—	2
Heligoland	30·12	59	2	WSW.	2	3	1	b	—	—	2

PROBABLE.

Tuesday. SCOTLAND. *Wednesday.*
W. to N. and E., fresh to moderate. | W. to N. and E., moderate. Fine.
Generally fine.

IRELAND.
W. to N. and E., light to moderate. | NE. to SE. and SW., light to fresh.
Fine.

WEST CENTRAL.
W. to NNE., moderate. Fine. | As next above. Generally fine.

SW. ENGLAND.
NW. to N. and E., variable, light to | NE. to SE. and SW., moderate. Fine.
moderate. Fine.

SE. ENGLAND.
As next above. | NE. to SE., moderate to light. Fine.

EAST COAST.
Similar to above. | NW. to E., moderate. Fine.

Explanation.

B.—Barometer corrected and reduced to 32° at mean sea level ; each ten feet, of vertical rise, causing about one hundredth of an inch *diminution*; and each ten degrees, above 32°, causing nearly three hundredths *increase.* E.—Exposed thermometer in shade. D.—Difference of moistened bulb (for evaporation and dew point). W.—Wind direction (true — two points *left* of magnetic). F.—Force (1 to 12 — estimated). X.—Extreme Force since last report. C.—Cloud (1 to 9). I.—Initials: b.—blue sky; c.—clouds (detached); f.—fog; h.—hail; l.—lightning; m.—misty (hazy); o.—overcast (dull); r.—rain; s.—snow; t.—thunder. H.—Hours of R=Rainfall, or snow or hail (melted), since last report. S.—Sea-disturbance (1 to 9). Z.—Calm.

Extract from Beaufort Scale ; with additions.

1 = b = blue (sky).
2 = c = clouds (detached).
3 = f = fog, foggy.
4 = h = hail.
5 = m = misty (haze).
6 = o = overcast.

7 = r = rain, rainy.
8 = s = snow.
9 = t = thunder. Lightning.
And a line under, or a dash, or a dot. or repetition (as r r) is for MUCH of either character.

Fig 8. Weather Report

So he started the distribution of barometers around the coast together with a detailed, but readable, booklet entitled *Barometer and Weather Guide,* which included some of the useful sayings well known to mariners such as those quoted above. He also started writing the more academic *Weather Book* as part of his drive to be recognised by the scientific world. The demand for barometers, from harbour masters, local vicars and RNLI stations far outstripped supply since there was no adequate budget for this scheme. Often FitzRoy spent his own money to meet some of these appeals. The proper use of the barometer and its ready availability were of a great help to all those on land, but did not cater for those already at sea. FitzRoy's answer was to set up a warning system comprising drums and cones (see Fig 8.) to be hoisted on large gantries placed at strategic locations around the coast. These warned of impending storms and the wind direction associated with them. Easily stated, this was a massive undertaking. The telegraph, and the cooperation of many telegraph companies, was essential to the process. The speediest way of operating the system was for coastal telegraph stations to be responsible for receiving the warnings, for raising and lowering the cones and drums and for advising local coastguards that a warning had been received. Some were sceptical that mere telegraph clerks would be capable of such work. They were proved wrong; the clerks did an excellent job.

By 1860 there were eighteen weather stations sending in information and receiving storm warnings, and the number was rising rapidly. The need for these warnings was clear for all to see; losses of life at sea around the

United Kingdom coast stood at over 850 a year, to say nothing of the loss of ships and their cargoes. However, the storm warning system was not received with universal approval. Two main groups were unhappy with these developments. Many in the scientific community complained that this forecasting had no scientific basis. The purpose of the Statist's office, they said, was to provide data so that it would be possible for them to find a law of weather; attempts at forecasting the weather were premature and invalid. FitzRoy himself coined the term forecasts, about which he said, "Predictions and prophecies they are not, the term forecast is strictly applicable to such an opinion as is the result of scientific combination and calculation". It was crystal clear to FitzRoy that a forecast concerned the probability of an event happening while a prediction was a definitive statement that it would occur; others saw the two terms as virtually synonymous. At the same time the data that was still flooding in from ships' logs was gathering dust and not being properly processed. The Royal Society felt they had invested their reputation in the Statist's office and were wary of it being seriously damaged. Nor were commercial interests happy. Those who owned fleets of colliers, or fishing boats, or ferries found their ships tied up in port because a storm was forecast. Sometimes the storm did not arrive and they were out of pocket. Notable among these relentless critics was the MP Augustus Smith who raised his concerns in the House of Commons at every conceivable opportunity. Figures suggest that around this time over fifty MPs had major shipping interests. It may be a little unfair to some to generalise, but many, even most, ship owners put profit before anything else including the lives of their crews. Some background for this assertion is given at Annex.

THE ROYAL CHARTER

1859 proved something of a crunch year for FitzRoy. First, he was working himself into the ground planning and overseeing the schemes described above. He still craved a position among the scientific elite so he was still wrestling with the problem of finding some sort of over-arching law for the weather. While all this was going on some crucial events occurred in that year. The first concerned the loss of the ironclad steam clipper the *Royal Charter*. She was one of a new class of sailing ship that boasted auxiliary steam power, especially to speed her transit through the doldrums. She was sailing to Liverpool from Melbourne carrying many returning miners who had made their fortunes in the Australian gold rush which started in 1851, and their pockets were literally full of gold. She was struck by a particularly powerful storm from the north east and was wrecked off the Isle of Anglesey. Over 400 of those on board died. No less than 342 ships of various sizes were lost in the storm. The disaster received massive publicity, in no small part due to the popularity of the *Illustrated London News,* which covered the story in detail with dramatic woodcuts depicting the last moments of the vessel. Additionally, Charles Dickens gave the event considerable coverage in his widely read periodicals. At the subsequent Inquiry

FitzRoy was critical of the actions of the captain who, he thought, should have stood out to sea away from a lee shore. FitzRoy also showed that the storm could easily have been forecast because of exceptional pressure and temperature differences recorded between his northerly and southerly weather stations. These highlighted the contrast between a sweltering London and, simultaneously, snow falling in Yorkshire. The disaster occurred just as reluctant agreement had been reached about setting up FitzRoy's storm warning system, in no small part due to the impact of the Black Sea Storm which had occurred just five years earlier. The Golden Wreck, as the disaster became known, effectively swept away much of the lingering resistance to the scheme. By 1861 the initial fifty warning stations had been increased to 130.

Fig 9. Shipwreck of the SS *Stanley* in 1864
off Tynemouth, North East England

THE ORIGIN OF SPECIES

For FitzRoy, at a personal level, another momentous event took place that year. Charles Darwin (1809-1872) finally published *The Origin of Species*. It was a body blow to FitzRoy who was a fundamentalist Christian, along with many other eminent people. For him, the book was the most awful blasphemy for it was seen as striking at the very roots of Christianity. And who had facilitated this damnable book? FitzRoy himself!

THE PROBLEMS MULTIPLY

As the forecasts produced by the Statist's office became more widely read – *The Times* started publishing them in 1861 – it was clear that, although many were accurate and lifesaving, some were wrong. FitzRoy could claim over 70% success for some areas, but that meant something near 30% were in error and some of the major fleet owners were gunning for him. The MP Augustus Smith has been mentioned above; he owned a fleet of colliers and the ferry to the Isles of Scilly. But some, within the scientific community, were also most unhappy with the whole gamut of FitzRoy's activities. A leader among these was Francis Galton (later Sir Francis) (1822-1911) at the Royal Society who was angry that so much data was accumulating in the Statist's office, but not being processed. A total of 5,500 months of data had so far been sent in by 800 ships. Galton was very much a man of the Enlightenment, believing absolutely in inductive methods of progressing science. He was also conscious that the Royal Society was closely tied into FitzRoy's office and so could, by association, be subject to ridicule when forecasts were wrong. We may also note that, at a more personal level, a deep distrust had developed between the two men in part because Galton was Charles Darwin's half cousin and thus, for FitzRoy, closely linked with the liberal Darwin family and the concept of evolution.

Not un-typically, questions of funding brought matters to a head. The original uncertainty about who was in control led the Royal Society to make calls for an assessment of Value for Money from the Statist. In 1863 that review was undertaken, with Galton in the Chair. Several aspects of the review were disingenuous at best. As an example, various stretches of coast were chosen for examination such as that between Scarborough and Berwick. FitzRoy had forecast a gale for this area, which included a number of reporting stations. A few recorded a full gale while others reported high winds of varying strengths. However, the Inquiry only scored these struck by the full gale and thus came up with a low percentage figure of success. FitzRoy objected strenuously to this manipulation of the data, but to no avail. The full Report was published in 1864 and FitzRoy was pilloried. *The Times* turned into a caustic critic and discontinued their forecasts. Galton was triumphant, as were the leaders of the commercial lobby. As a result many outlying stations were closed and the storm warning system was abandoned. Newspapers stopped issuing forecasts. The seafarers were up in arms but their voices counted for little. Power and influence in Victorian Britain won the day.

FitzRoy saw all his dreams shattered. He wasn't recognised as a great scientist. He was responsible for taking Darwin round the world and hence for the theory of evolution. His efforts on behalf of sailors had been cast aside. He was virtually penniless. On 30th April 1864, he committed suicide.

Mounting pressure grew for the reinstatement of the storm warnings. But the scientific community would not budge. The committee that had produced the damming report stated that the forecasts were "not generally correct in point of fact" and that there was "no evidence of their utility". Demands that the services should recommence were led by an MP, Colonel Sykes. He championed the cause throughout 1865 and was unsparing in his criticism of the scientific community. It was he who railed against the "pedantic affectation of science" especially when the committee proposed the establishment of eight further observatories with the aim of being able to predict storms based on philosophical data rather than empirical data. Their time scale for achieving this goal was fifteen years! Some meteorologists, such as Glaisher, lent their support to Sykes, but it was not until the end of 1867 that his efforts bore fruit with the announcement that storm warnings would be reintroduced in January 1868. Full public recognition for the pioneering efforts of FitzRoy came in 2002 when he became the only person, rather than geographic location, to have one of the United Kingdom's shipping forecast areas named after him.

10. THE PROBLEMS OF EMPIRE - INDIA

Importance of India – Tropical cyclones –
Forecasting monsoons – Patterns of oscillation

Efforts to understand the weather were not confined to the Western world. India was the jewel in the crown of the British Empire and the 1850s saw the reinforcement of this position. The East India Company transferred authority for the running of the country to the British Government and Queen Victoria was crowned Empress of India in 1876. On the subcontinent the monsoon – the word means season – absolutely dictates the pattern of life for millions. Its formation is similar to a massive sea breeze. As temperatures rise in summer, warm, moist air is swept up from the south west bringing with it the heavy rainfall which is essential for agriculture. In winter the process reverses and the north east monsoon brings cool, dry air and clear skies. The region is also subject to violent cyclonic storms which can cause havoc in low-lying coastal areas. A number of authorities set out to explain the local cyclonic phenomenon. Among these was Colonel James Capper (1743-1825) of the East India Company. His work, *Observations on the Winds and Monsoons*, published in 1801, muddied the waters, certainly those of the Indian Ocean. He produced limited data that seemed to show that the storms were actually whirlwinds that were both short-lived and local, seldom exceeding 120 miles in diameter. These misconceptions were questioned by William Reid, already mentioned, and largely overturned by the efforts of Henry Piddington (1797-1858). He was an experienced sea captain and polymath who became the Head of Maine Law in Calcutta. He coined the term cyclone believing this meant a coiled serpent and his aim was to produce guidance for mariners when they encountered storms in the Bay of Bengal. He studied the wind patterns around these cyclones and correctly described their movement. This he drew up in a hornbook, a type of publication made from flattened sheep horns and more usually found in the classroom because it was robust and cheaper than using paper. He added a form of protractor so a ship's captain could place himself within the storm and see the best course to steer for safety. His work gained added recognition after the cyclone of 1864, which caused a forty-foot rise in sea level in Calcutta where some 50,000 people lost their lives. Of the 195 ships in the harbour there only twenty-three were undamaged.

There are few places in the world where a single weather phenomena so completely dominates all aspects of a region's life as is the case of the south west monsoon in the Indian subcontinent. The cyclone of 1864 led to the setting up of State meteorological centres and these were then combined into the Indian National Meteorological Department. However, cyclones, though very damaging, were an irregular feature of life. It was the two annual monsoons that made or destroyed the lives of so many. The monsoon is not restricted to India; its impact is felt across a wide swathe of countries at that latitude but it is not surprising that, at least in the United Kingdom, it is seen as essentially an Indian phenomenon. The new National Department was headed by Henry Blandford (1834-1893). Blandford produced a number of reports but largely relied on measurements of the snowfall in the Himalayas to predict the likely strength of the summer monsoon. There had been a series of very weak monsoons in a country that was utterly dependent on their regular arrival. The years 1876 and 1878 had been particularly dry and starvation was widespread. Sadly, it has to be said that the reaction of the British administration to these crises was often less than sympathetic. Indeed, the Viceroy at the time, Lord Lytton, appeared unable, or unwilling, to realise the level of misery all around him; it has been estimated that over five million people died of starvation yet wheat was still exported to Britain. Lytton was mainly driven by a desire to reduce the amount of money spent on welfare and he was sadly successful in achieving that goal. A cartoon depicting a starving group with the words: "We are starving, and still they demand their taxes" summed up the situation all too well. To further compound the operational shortcomings of the Department, Blandford saw the large Indian subcontinent as the ideal laboratory for trying to gain understanding of the weather in general - for the benefit of British scientists rather than the local inhabitants. The figures for snowfalls in the Himalayas had already been shown as an irrelevant statistic in any attempt to calculate the strength of the monsoon. The same was true of sunspot activity. A spectacular but entirely coincidental success was scored using this method in 1885, but more serious attempts to forecast this life and death feature of Indian life had to wait for the arrival of Gilbert Walker (1868-1958) as Head of the Department.

Walker was a child prodigy and it was as a child that he got his nickname of Boomerang. He had been given a boomerang and was puzzled by its flight which he thought could be explained mathematically. He went up to Cambridge at the age of fourteen where he was also especially interested in the reaction of colliding spherical objects. It was said that if the weather was fine, he would be outside throwing his boomerang and if it was wet he would be inside playing billiards. He was selected to head the Indian Meteorological Department and arrived there in 1904. It was an appointment that caused raised eyebrows in several quarters. What did he know of the weather, let alone India? He arrived at a time when the shadow of failed monsoons hung heavily over the country. Walker was not impressed by the methods then used to predict the rainfall to be expected during the monsoon. He saw the phenomenon as much wider than simply as it related to the subcontinent. As a mathematician and statistician he pored over masses of figures ever further from India. He particularly noted certain pressure patterns as far away as Tahiti and Darwin in Australia. There was an oscillation between high and low pressure at these two locations, which seemed to correlate with the strength of the monsoon. He was not certain quite how this worked but, on his departure from India, he said that he knew he was on the right track. He predicted that it would be for someone following him to describe the how and the why. That someone was to be Jacob Bjorknes, who we meet later, who linked Walker's findings with ENSO, the El Nino Southern Oscillation, naming that variation in the zonal pressure gradient the Walker Oscillation. Walker, on his return to the United Kingdom, went on to establish various other oscillatory patterns including that of the North Atlantic. The Walker Institute at Reading University is named after him. An understanding of oscillating patterns of weather currently looms large in meteorology.

PATTERNS OF OSCILLATION

Human beings have always been drawn to the idea of cyclical patterns. Day and night, the annual calendar, even birth, maturity and death; these form the boundaries of our lives. It is not surprising then that we look for patterns in both weather and climate.

The work done on patterns of oscillation by Jacob Bjorknes (or Jack as he was known when he became a naturalised American in 1939) was as remarkable as that he had undertaken as a young man at the Bergen School, which is discussed below. He realised that the sea surface temperatures at the eastern side of the Pacific were surprisingly low for that latitude. As a result there was a linked thermal circulation in the atmosphere above the sea right across the Pacific. He saw this combination of air and ocean circulations as an oscillating pattern with the east-west variations in temperature gradients both driving and then being driven by the variations.

Bjorknes' insights, as well as those of Walker, explained a phenomenon that had a long history. *El Niño* was the name given to it by the Peruvians on the west coast of South America. They noted that, periodically, sea surface temperatures rose, disrupting the food chain and driving fish away from the coastal region. This seemed to coincide with Christmas, hence the name *El Niño* or Christ Child. It became clear that ENSO had three phases. As well as *El Niño*, with its warmer coastal water along the western seaboard of South America, there was, at the other end of the spectrum, a period when especially cold water was found in this region. This is the *La Niña*, or little girl, case. There was also a normal period between these two extremes when the prevailing easterly wind drove water westwards starting the whole process. As these easterly winds slacken – and we are not sure why this happens – so the weight of water in the western Pacific sloshes back to the east, stopping the upwelling of colder water and triggering *El Niño*. Oceanographers are trying to pick out a cycle from data gathered over the last 150 years. Some now quote a three to four year pattern, but the establishment of a reliable figure has, to date, eluded them.

The impact of these oscillations is felt not just off the coast of Peru. The effect is also felt along the west coast of North America and, to a lesser extent, into the Caribbean.

As a result, a massive array of buoys is now in place in the Pacific to monitor sea temperatures as a means of predicting future ENSO events. By the 1960s interest had steadily grown on the subject of oscillatory currents. Others were noted; for example, the Indian Ocean Dipole and the Pacific Decadal Oscillation. Such oscillations appear to occur over many different time periods. They are simultaneously oceanic and atmospheric and there are clear, if poorly understood, teleconnections between them. A wide range of influences cause their variations and it is difficult to disentangle cause and effect. Might it be that hidden somewhere within all this interaction, there lies a Law of Oscillations waiting to be explained by some great weatherman – or woman – at some future date?

What is remarkable in all this is the level of understanding achieved many years before either Gilbert Walker or Jacob Bjorknes arrived on the scene. Edmund Halley (1656-1742) was a great traveller who is known in part because there is a comet named after him. He had many other claims to fame, including the invention of a diving bell. He correctly identified the pattern of the trade winds across the globe and used a Mercator chart to plot them. The Mercator projection is commonplace today, but its usefulness was barely recognised then. It is the trade winds in the southern Pacific that trigger ENSO. Halley believed the winds were driven by diurnal variations in temperature and it took another polymath to correct this error. He was George Hadley (1685-1768) who realised that it was the earth's rotation that caused these persistent air flows. Hadley also wondered why the desert regions were not at the hottest part of the earth, the equator, but some degrees north and south of it. The pattern of descending air at those latitudes which causes this are now called the Hadley cells. To these two great and original thinkers must be added the name of Alexander von Humboldt (1769-1859). As a traveller and climatologist, he was one of the most authoritative figures of his time. His stance was different from that of many scientists when he said: "Measure everything without extinguishing the wonder they inspire". He also saw nature as a "global force interwoven as with a thousand threads." We may well substitute weather for nature as such a force. While in South America he studied the ocean currents off the western coast and accurately plotted their flow. The whole is properly known as the Humboldt Current, itself an integral part of ENSO.

11. REAL PROGRESS

The continuing search for a synoptic chart – Forecasting methods – Origins of the Bergen School – Wind circulation – Fronts – School Alumni

We have already seen how attempts to draw synoptic weather charts were hampered by three main difficulties. One was obtaining synchronous observations covering a wide area, and having them promptly if they were to have any value for forecasting the weather. The telegraph largely solved this problem. The second was to have a sufficient number of observations to avoid large gaps in the plot. This last was both an organisational and a financial issue. Meteorologists always want more readings, but, by the second half of the 19th century, the problem was well on the way to a solution, at least in the western world. Translating the data into a useable form was the third hurdle that had to be cleared. It presupposed an understanding of the general pattern of the weather as well as subjects such as which way the wind blew around a depression. As we have seen, this last remained a topic of considerable debate.

FitzRoy's main antagonist, Galton, was a brilliant child. Brought up as a Quaker, he was reading well at the age of two and had a good smattering of Latin and Greek by the age of six. But he himself was conscious of the fine line between genius and insanity. He suffered a particularly deep depression at the time of his father's death when he was just twenty-two. He travelled widely and became known as a skilled and entertaining writer of travel books. As a statistician, he was very much in favour of the Baconian method of induction and was entirely against any idea of forecasting until a law of weather had been established. Aware of the irritation felt by those who had to work their way through columns of figures, he was anxious to produce charts but these, given his scepticism about forecasting, were essentially observational charts. He tried a variety of styles in his massive work *Meteorographica* but the symbology of his early attempts was convoluted and obscure. However, he did coin the term anti-cyclone for an area of higher pressure, now universally used but a source of derision at the time. We have already seen how Galton and FitzRoy crossed swords over the issue of forecasting and, in a sense, Galton may be said to have won. He moved on to study fingerprinting but he is better remembered for his work on eugenics, a term he coined. He disliked averages and protested about the human tendency of revision to mediocrity. Surely, he said, it was both possible and desirable to establish a master race. His influence continued into the 20th century; the results are all too well known.

Yet various forms of charts had already been produced across the Atlantic. Mention of Elias Loomis was made when considering the dispute between Espy and Redfield. Loomis, who championed the study of meteorology, had watched this continuing spat with interest and had concluded that the vast extent of continental United States, with its expanding telegraph network, provided the perfect location for setting up an extensive network of observation locations. Some networks had existed as early as 1814 at Army posts but the telegraph allowed synchronous observations of storms to be plotted, their tracks assessed and warnings issued for those in the line of fire. Putting this theory into practice fell to the newly founded Smithsonian Institution. In 1848 Joseph Henry (1797-1878) was appointed the first Secretary and he brought with him a longstanding interest in meteorology. He immediately set up a system as envisaged by Loomis calling for volunteers to collect the data. He soon had over 600 people sending in their records. This group also sent in natural history specimens and asked a wide range of weather related questions all but swamping the small staff available to answer them. By 1856 the data was displayed for all to see and was also made available to newspapers. The programme was severely curtailed during the American Civil War which started in 1861. At the end of the war it was taken over by the US Army and then became the National Weather Service in 1891. The success of the system led many to claim that Loomis, who initiated the scheme, can justifiably be called the United States most renowned meteorologist. However, the system was essentially geared to the tracking of storms rather than to the wider need for forecasting weather in general. We may note that it led to a preference for so-called continuity forecasting as the norm. Such a method has strengths, but it is also based on assumptions about the future behaviour of weather patterns, which remains a major weakness. Some of the various forecasting methods are discussed in the next section.

Back in Europe the luxury of a landmass upwind of incoming storms did not exist. In these circumstances the drawing of charts simple enough to be useful yet not so simple that they told one little, was proving to be more difficult than it seemed. As a result the inclusion of lines of equal pressure, the isobars, by Galton was based on such a paucity of observations, and their complete absence to the westward, that they were at best guesswork and at worst quite misleading. This same charge was levelled at Edme Marie-Davy (1820-1893), a French chemist and inventor credited with producing the first periscope. From the 1860s he was Deputy Director of the Paris Observatory in charge of meteorology and he too was anxious to improve the drawing up of charts. He had taken over from Liais who had done work on the Black Sea storm, but he did not favour Le Verrier's liking for atmospheric tidal waves, rather aligning himself with FitzRoy's approach. FitzRoy was happy to have his book on weather translated into French to reinforce this alliance. His willingness to exchange information with the French led to him being presented with a magnificent clock, now held at the Met Office in Exeter. The findings of the Bergen School were to help solve the surface chart question; upper air charts were still many years away.

There were exceptions to the rule about the production of charts. Alexander Buchan (1829-1907) saw the plotting of isobars as a crucial part of completing weather maps, and we know him to be right. He produced a set of diagrams showing the track of a depression that crossed the Atlantic in 1868; they are immediately recognisable today. He was a central figure in the Scottish Meteorological Society and he wrote a standard text on the weather called *The Handy Book of Meteorology*. The introduction to the book makes interesting reading. It is full of Victorian "onwards and upwards"; problems will be solved! At the same time Buchan was highly critical of the British education system where meteorological studies were considered to be of very little account. Have things changed? What level of knowledge is called for in current schools' syllabi? As a simple example: How many owners of aneroid barometers have made the necessary height adjustments to them or even know that such adjustments are necessary to ensure the barometer reads sea level pressure?

FORECASTING METHODS

The term weather forecasting meant different things to different people, as it still does today. The way of achieving it depended on the would-be forecaster's scientific background, the geography of their workplace, the method in vogue at the time and sometimes the economic constraints under which they were working. Those trying to establish whether forecasting was possible noted that science, and especially astronomy, had made great strides in the 17th century such that events like eclipses could be measured with precision. As discussed above, there are good reasons why it was not possible to find the same level of precision with weather forecasting.

Notwithstanding the scientific, religious and astrological crosscurrents that swirled around the science of meteorology, it is still possible to offer some classification of the varying approaches to the art of weather forecasting. There was the astrological approach mentioned above which also interacted with the 19th century debate on the difference between prediction and prophesy. The latter was overlaid with religious sensitivities. The prophets were the medium though which God communicated his intentions, especially those concerned with warnings about conduct and future retribution for the unrighteous. Any prediction needed to avoid trespassing on such holy ground. This was, in part, one reason for Admiral FitzRoy coining the term forecasting, a probabilistic statement set against prediction which was a term implying certainty. With this backdrop, various methodologies for forecasting were developed over the years.

Continuity Forecasting is simply a way of observing the weather in one location, assessing its speed and direction of movement and then carrying it forward along the movement vector. Such a method can be refined by attempting to predict changes in the direction of movement and hence about future tracks. These procedures had some relevance to large landmasses where the airflow is predominantly west to east and where there is some commonality in the landscape. For the United Kingdom such an approach clearly has limited value. Continuity methods have to be modified in various ways. For example, surface weather charts need to be adjusted since weather systems are subject to friction close to the ground. This effect changes such things as wind speed and direction up to heights of about 3,000 feet. Without this adjustment a false track can easily be plotted.

A rather different approach is to use Analogous Forecasting. Here, after plotting the latest observations, a search is made of previous charts to find one that is similar to the current one. Once this is found the assumption is made that what happened in the earlier situation will be repeated in the future. Those supporting the concept of Chaos Theory, which is discussed below, would suggest that history as well as weather does not, indeed cannot, repeat itself. Other pitfalls exist. For example, how close a match is close enough? Even using the amazing power of super-computers such a method remains of dubious value.

Many of the textbooks produced in the first half of the 20th century suggested a forecasting approach combining elements of the above methods but still including room for the experienced forecaster to exercise some judgement. As an example, Sverre Pettersson (1898-1974), a product of the Bergen School (see below), offered eighteen rules and an eight-step procedure for the forecaster to follow in his widely used textbook of 1941 *Introduction to Meteorology*.

In some ways Computer Modelling has now overtaken some of these more basic methods. It is the latest development in the concept of Numerical Weather

Prediction (NWP), which had its origins in the early 20th century, but which only became possible with the advent of powerful computers in the 1960s. This topic is covered in detail in later pages.

A further subdivision is noteworthy since it coloured much discussion in the latter part of the 19th century. It concerns the difference between Storm Intelligence and Storm Prediction. The former was descriptive, stating when and where a storm has occurred. This would often be too late for many people to have time to take any effective action. It was, for some in the scientific community, all that was possible or, indeed, desirable since no general law of the weather existed. But it was the prediction that a storm was brewing together with its likely future path and intensity that all seafarers so desperately wanted. As we have seen, there were those, such as FitzRoy, who believed Storm Prediction to be possible.

We may also note that carrying out any assessment of the accuracy of forecasts derived using the above methods is fraught with difficulties. Forecasts covered a range of elements; wind speed and direction, temperature, pressure, visibility, cloud amounts, sea temperature among them. How many of these had to be correct for the whole forecast to be declared as accurate? How close had they to be in space and time to the indicated location? The situation with storms was rather simpler because the number of elements was reduced, essentially to two, wind speed and direction of movement. But even here difficulties remain since small changes in wind speed and storm track may turn out to have major consequences for those likely to be affected.

THE BERGEN SCHOOL

A final solution to the question of wind movements around an extra-tropical storm and a method of drawing an accurate and readable weather chart came together in the work of that remarkable establishment the Bergen Geophysical Institute in Norway, often known as the Bergen School. To understand the success of the School it is first necessary to review the life of its founder Vilhelm Bjorknes (1862-1951). Bjorknes' father was a hydrologist and from quite an early age Vilhelm helped his father in his work. He then undertook studies in Paris and in Bonn where he worked under Hertz, known for the scale of radio frequencies which bear his name. And it was here that Bjorknes' interest in wave motions in the sea and in the air was stimulated. Lectures he gave at MIT in the United States and in Oslo on *Dynamic Meteorology and Hydrology* caused something of a stir and his published works on the subject greatly impressed a number of German scientists so much so that they invited him in 1912 to join the staff of the University of Leipzig. At the start of the First World War many of the German scientists there were called up and Bjorknes brought his son Jacob (1897-1975), aged eighteen, and another young Norwegian, Halvar Solberg (1895-1974) to help him. He stayed there until 1917. As a strong internationalist, he was greatly distressed by the War and jumped at the chance to return to Norway with his son and Solberg when the famous Norwegian explorer Nansen suggested he set up a meteorological school in Bergen.

His decision to do so was partly assisted by Nils Gustave Eckholm (1848-1923), a keen and skilled aerologist who was famous for his involvement in the ill-fated attempt at a trans-polar balloon flight by the Norwegian SA Andree. Eckholm championed the use of isallobars – lines joining points of equal pressure change. He did so in part in reaction to slow progress with improvements in forecasting since isallobars can indicate the likely direction of movement of weather systems. However, isallobars can paint quite different pictures dependent on what period is chosen over which to measure the change.

Vilhelm Bjorknes' approach to meteorology was very much that of the mathematician; his son's ideas were rather less theoretical. Jacob's paper, written in conjunction with Solberg and entitled *Life Cycle of Cyclones and the Polar Front Theory of Atmospheric Circulation*, must rank as one of the most important meteorological documents ever written. It was completed in 1922 and was concerned with the movement of extra-tropical cyclones. These low-pressure areas are not hurricanes, typhoons or tropical cyclones, which are all exactly the same phenomena and all form in equatorial latitudes drawing their immense energy from the sea. The extra-tropical cyclones form between latitudes of about 30 degrees and 60 degrees north or south of the equator and it is these that regularly track across Europe.

The School was an outstanding success. This has been put down in part to the happy environment generated by the Bjorknes family and by the way Vilhelm drew in talented young scientists and then gave them their head. Jacob came up with ideas about the structure and movement of extra-tropical cyclones, depicting the concept of a squall line. This developed into consideration of frontal systems, so called because they were "battle grounds" between air masses of different temperatures and thus reminiscent of the fronts of the First World War. Additionally, the idea of a life cycle of a depression was born. Jacob Bjorknes did not work on this alone. Apart from Halvor Solberg, a gifted young man called Tor Bergeron (1891-1977) offered ideas concerning air masses. The concept of blocks of largely homogenous air was not in fact new. As far back as 1780 Erasmus Darwin (1731-1802), pondering on his own records of the weather, had suggested "districts" of air where conditions were similar. Bergeron also established the process whereby occlusions formed, these being frontal lines where all the warmer air is lifted clear of the ground. He also set out the symbols used on charts to mark frontal lines. This last is now standard practice but originated from the need to use symbols rather than colours since colour printing was expensive. Bergeron was later to become well known for work on cloud physics which was refined by the German Walter Findeison (1909-1945) in a process which now carries their two names. The wealth of team talent was well expressed when it was said: "The depression is born of Solberg's initial wave, develops as Jacob Bjorknes' extra-typical cyclone and suffers death in Bergeron's occlusion."

Other members of the School will be mentioned later. Another story told by Vilhelm Bjorknes is indicative of life at the School. He said: "We were having difficulty finding a new stove boy. My old brain could not keep up with the younger assistants. So I tended the stove. I wished to keep the fires burning – spiritually and materially." He always took the long view, though one based on a certainty that accurate forecasting for considerable periods ahead would definitely come about. He said: "It would take years to drill a tunnel through a mountain. Many workers would not witness the breakthrough. Nevertheless, this will not bar others from later riding through the tunnel at express train speed."

12. THE DATA COLLECTORS

Amassing data – Sheer joy of keeping records –
Rainfall – Snowflakes – CET – The Antarctic

For many individuals the collection of weather data is rather like assembling any collection of precious items, or indeed stamps or train numbers. There is the interest, and pleasure, in building up a growing body of items and, in the case of weather, data. And this data is both endless and free! The records gathered are essentially daily observations and their value lies in part in providing information about specific events such as storms or floods. More important perhaps, is the accumulated picture they paint; in other words what their data says about the climate.

The process of writing descriptive accounts of the weather took a major step forward with improved printing techniques and with the production and distribution of newspapers and magazines. It was Daniel Defoe (1660-1731) who first took advantage of these advances in terms of weather reporting. Released from jail in early 1703 and desperately short of funds, he cast about for a money-spinner. The Great Storm of November

1703 provided the ideal answer. This storm covered a large part of the southern United Kingdom and caused extensive damage both as a result of high winds but also through storm surges around the coast. It is estimated that up to 10,000 people lost their lives, many at sea. Defoe called for anyone affected by the storm to send him their experiences and these he converted into a book of authentic accounts entitled simply *The Storm*. Some experiences may have been exaggerated as has sometimes been suggested but it is worth noting that few if any of those whose accounts he used protested at the time about any inaccuracies. Recent studies have shown that many of the more extreme reports were entirely credible. Regardless of that, they were certainly meticulously researched and recorded. Paradoxically, Defoe detested the value the Enlightenment placed on reason saying that the storm "blew out the candle of reason leaving them all in the dark." His aim was to use the event to preach God's wrath. Yet here he was gathering data in a way which would have delighted Bacon! This pattern of descriptive recording was to be followed with the collection of much more precise data in the next century when instruments became more readily available.

THE RAIN

Some enthusiasts were able to come together and share their records, others were essentially solitary observers. Many of those in both categories followed the path of George Symons who famously said: "There was no great goal, only the innocent enjoyment of an inexhaustible subject". Even so, some did set out on this demanding path conscious that they were expanding the corpus of scientific knowledge. Various weather phenomena attracted these gatherers of data. Rainfall was one such and this was the field to which George Symons (1838-1900) brought both his enthusiasm and his organising ability. He was a precocious young man who kept a weather diary from an early age. At seventeen he joined the Royal Meteorological Society, addressing them on the topic of thunderstorms and the rain to which they gave rise. He worked for a short while in the Met Office, but displeased the then Head, FitzRoy, because of his fixation with rainfall figures. For the Victorians of this time much emphasis was given to the dark, dismal and threatening nature of the weather. Symons swam against this tide rejoicing in rain's life-giving and refreshing nature. He would certainly have been pleased to know that people still use the phrase; "As Right as Rain".

He was by no means the first to try and measure rainfall. Richard Towneley (1629-1707), another true polymath, kept a 15 year record from his home in Lancashire and tried to encourage others in what he described as a very simple task. He drew deductions from rainfall patterns, for example to do with rain shadows where the lee side of high ground is always drier than the windward side. He was also in regular contact with William Derham (1657-1735), Rector of Upminster, well known for striking a balance between the methodologies of the Enlightenment and a belief in an all-powerful God saying: "Man was made to observe and set forth the glory

GEORGE JAMES SYMONS, F.R.S.
(*President* 1880-1 and 1900)
BORN AUGUST 6, 1838.   DIED MARCH 10, 1900.

Fig 10. George Symons

of the infinite Creator." Their exchanges helped shed light on the impact of the Great Storm of 1703.

At the end of 1863 Symons wrote to *The Times* calling for volunteers to record rainfall figures, offering them instruments and the attendant forms. And volunteers there were aplenty. By 1867 he had 1,300 observers in what became the British Rainfall Organisation. They came from both sexes, all classes and were of all ages. By the time he died in 1900 there were 3,408 stations sending in regular figures. None of this came about without a rigorous approach to accuracy and a great deal of tact. His observers, few of whom knew each other, were all volunteers who needed constant encouragement to continue their work regardless of weather conditions but whose standards of observation had to be of the highest order if the record was to have any value. He labelled them authorities and adopted a very democratic approach, regularly seeking the views of his all-amateur team and then acting on what they suggested. The agreed daily time for taking observations was reached in this way. His insistence on absolute precision was a key factor in retaining the loyalty of all those involved. As an example, he assembled, with the help of the vicar, the Reverend Griffiths, no less than 40 rain gauges in the Rectory grounds at Strafield Turgis in Hampshire to try to assess the optimum size for gauges. The result was an instrument with a diameter of 8 inches, a figure which has remained the standard size to the present day. He was also involved in helping with the introduction of the Stevenson Screen for housing meteorological instruments, the white box with louvered sides standing 4.1 feet above the ground which is still a common sight today.

The results of his labours, and those of his authorities, was the publication of detailed annual rainfall figures and a magazine. The latter, together with a small grant from the Royal Society, allowed the organisation to stay afloat and to stay independent. It was eventually incorporated into the Met Office and continued in existence until 1991. It gives a stupendous record almost unrivalled in meteorological history overshadowing the many worthy efforts of other, smaller groups of weather data collectors. Symons served as President of the Royal Meteorological Society almost to the end of his life. His work, perhaps offers an example to all those who run voluntary organisations: Listen to, and respect, the views of your team but insist on the highest standards of work.

THE SNOW

Most of those who recorded aspects of the weather, with great diligence and commitment, did so alone. One such was Wilson Bentley (1865-1931). He was born in Jericho in north Vermont in the United States, well known for its severe winters. He received very little formal schooling but was taught at home by his mother. He proved to be a talented musician but his fame was not to lie in that direction. His mother owned a microscope and he was entranced by it. He started taking photos of snowflakes through the microscope and, after lengthy trial and error, eventually found a way of obtaining clear images. Over the following years he produced some 5,000 pictures of snowflakes, all of which showed the well-known hexagonal shape and all of them were different. He called them "tiny miracles of beauty". (See Fig 11.) But why were they all different? He analysed them with care noting such things as temperature, wind direction and relationship to the mountains but could come up with no clear answers. Not surprisingly he became known as Snowflake Bentley.

He was not the only one to try and unlock their secrets. James Glaisher was among others who had studied them without discovering the reasons for their diversity. In later life Bentley turned his attention to rain drops and, from scratch, developed ideas about the differences in their shapes and sizes. He realised that the tear-drop shape, still popular even on official weather maps, did not provide an accurate description of what we now know to be either a small sphere or a flat bottomed blob.

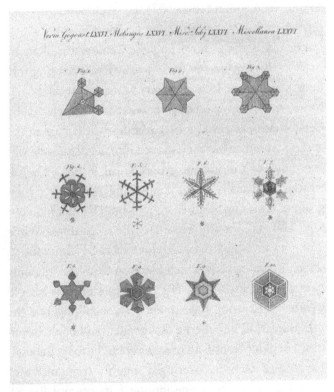

Fig 11. Snowflakes, Bentley's "Tiny miracles of beauty"

The record he produced of snowflakes was not only of major interest scientifically, it also contained pictures of rare beauty. That much-abused word 'awesome' is rightly applied to some of the massive and powerful weather phenomena; it can also be used to refer to some of its smallest manifestations.

THE CENTRAL ENGLAND TEMPERATURE RECORD

Among many other remarkable sets of climate data from several countries, one from the United Kingdom which stands out is the Central England Temperature Record (CET). This covers the period from 1659 for monthly figures and from 1722 for daily figures. It results from some extremely painstaking research completed by Gordon Manley (1902-1980). Manley worked for a time at the Met Office but then moved into academia. He was conscious of the impact geographical features had on weather, especially those concerning winds over high ground. He set up weather stations on hill and mountain tops and assiduously recorded their readings. While doing so he noted the behaviour of the Helm wind, a strong north-easterly which blows in Cumbria, the only named wind in Britain. His other passion was for old weather measuring instruments. Working against the prevailing tide, he believed that greater trust could be put in some older records than many thought to be the case. He studied records covering a roughly triangular area from Lancashire to a line joining London and Bristol. Notable among the records he used were those kept by Thomas Barker (1732-1809) who had taken note of pressure, temperature, cloud amounts and rainfall over a period of 60 years. These, and similar records, Manley analysed and corrected for a wide range of factors to arrive at a remarkably consistent set of numbers. These are still used as benchmarks today. Barker's record is amazing but it is not entirely unique. Other records exist, collected by hundreds, even thousands of un-named, unknown but hugely diligent individuals. For example, Radcliffe Observatory in Oxford can boast of a continuous record from 1815. The Observatory also displays a tower modelled on that of the Tower of the Winds in Athens, mentioned earlier. Further afield, Yale University has a record of temperature dating from 1777. The Hudson Bay Company required its employees, in all their far-flung stations in the Canadian Arctic to note weather conditions on a daily basis. Details of the first snowfalls and first thaws from the late 18th and early 19th centuries are thus available. Nor has this work ended. In the United Kingdom the Climatological Observers Link (COL) maintains the tradition. It has some 400 members and produces a monthly bulletin giving local data on a wide range of weather phenomena. The Royal Meteorological Society's WeatherClub and magazines such as Weather eYe provide further local data. In this electronic age, the United Kingdom Met Office has set up a free online community called the Weather Observation Website (WOW) where citizen scientists can upload observations; nearly 900 million of these have been received in the first four years of operation. In addition the photographic record, generated by the BBC's newly formed Weather Watchers crowd-sourced club, provides a current example of how deeply ingrained in society is this desire to perpetuate the fleeting moment that is the weather.

THE ANTARCTIC

We may rightly admire the data gatherers for their constancy, persistence and their insistence on accuracy. For most of them this calls, even in the electronic age, for a willingness to battle the elements on a daily basis. These forays into rain, wind and snow punctuate the day but they allow for a return to the fireside to mull over the day's findings. We should not forget those for whom an added factor is that of constant, real and ever present danger.

The British Antarctic Expedition of 1910 to 1913 set out to challenge one of the last uncharted areas of the globe. In one sense it ended in tragedy with the loss of life of Scott and his companions. Yet the aim of the expedition was not solely to reach the South Pole. There were also a number of scientific goals to be achieved. One was to conduct regular meteorological observations throughout the time in Antarctica and at all the locations supporting the push to the Pole. The leader of the meteorologists was George Simpson (1878-1965) and he and his men were required to amass as much data as possible in the most hostile of conditions – no fireside for them to return to. Nor was their personal equipment at all like that of today's explorers. Simpson's three-volume treatise recording the work was finally published in 1919 to great acclaim. It was clear that Scott had had the misfortune to be returning from the Pole during a period of exceptional cold, some 10°C lower than the average. Simpson became the Director of the Met Office in 1920 and it was he who produced the on-land version of the Beaufort wind scale. He was in post until 1938. A number of Antarctic features are named after him.

The Antarctic remains one of the great laboratories of the earth. Hidden within it lie many of the secrets of past climates. A number of scientists have spent long periods in this inhospitable region trying to unearth them and continue to do so today. One such is the Frenchman Claude Lorius (1932-). He observed bubbles rising from a discarded piece of ice core dropped into his drink of whiskey and he realised that therein lay the secret of ice core analysis. The bubbles contained oxygen trapped there tens of thousands of years earlier. Oxygen isotopes vary dependent on air temperature and thus it is possible to plot a graph of temperature change over time. Such is the stuff of scientific advances!

13. THE WORLD WARS

*First World War – Numerical Weather Prediction –
Between the wars – Second World War – Typhoon Cobra
and D Day – The Jet Stream – Unsung heroes*

THE FIRST WORLD WAR

At the start of the First World War, William Napier Shaw (1854-1945) had been in charge of the Met Office for some fifteen years. After graduating from Cambridge he spent almost twenty years at the Cavendish Laboratory in Cambridge before accepting the challenge of joining the Met Office. The Met Office had been in the doldrums for some time and, not surprisingly, he brought a strong, scientific approach to the work there. He produced a number of textbooks that reflected his mathematical background and worked, with only limited success, towards the introduction of metric measures for all weather recording.

At the start of the First World War it soon became apparent that the weather would play a significant role in all operations. The use of balloons for observing the fall of artillery shells was normal practise by this time; by 1918 some 13,000 balloons of various kinds, were being produced each month. But the growing importance of aircraft, initially for reconnaissance and later in both fighter and bomber roles, demanded a concomitant level of weather information. Shaw was approached and set up the Field Meteorological Service, known as Meteor R E, in France in 1915. Forecasts for the artillery remained a central task but, by the end of the war regular met observation flights were taking place reaching as high as 14,000 feet. These flights resulted in the generation of complex meteorological data forms not dissimilar to those in use over fifty years later. Another feature of the war that demanded the attention of meteorologists was the introduction of gas attacks. When to expect, and when to launch such attacks became part of all operational planning and this depended not only on wind direction, but also on pressure patterns and the likelihood of phenomena such as temperature inversions where an increase in temperature with height traps the air beneath.

Work on the battlefield threw up a number of talented meteorologists. Notable among these was Charles Douglas (1893-1982) an aviation and weather pioneer. His story continues into the Second World War where he played a vital role at the time of the D Day landings, advising James Stagg on the wisdom, or otherwise, of attempting an invasion on 5th June.

Shaw continued as Head of the Met Office as control passed from the Board of Trade to the Air Ministry. This organisational change gave it a public face since weather information was reported as "From the Air Ministry roof" in BBC broadcasts. In the early 1920s he introduced the tephigram chart for plotting upper air conditions;

it remains in use for the calculation of cloud base and cloud height. In 1926 he visited the Bergen School and Jacob Bjorknes then spent six months at the Met Office discussing his frontal weather theories. Somewhat strangely, Shaw later pronounced that: "Meteorologists have a natural aversion from the iteration of daily forecasting". Perhaps he was referring more to himself than the generality of his profession. He was certainly not averse to poking fun at others, remarking that to town dwellers the weather seemed to be of little importance, a matter more of curiosity, only verging on the important as the weekend approached.

NUMERICAL WEATHER PREDICTION (NWP)

Vilhelm Bjorknes could reasonably claim to have been the first man to believe that weather forecasting would be possible by the use of mathematical formulae. However, it was Lewis Fry Richardson (1881-1953) who carried this idea forward. NWP is made up of two elements. First there are the current atmospheric conditions from around the world, at sea level and above the earth; these are the initial conditions. Secondly there are seven, relatively simple physical laws that can be written as mathematical equations that describe how the elements interact and change over time.

Richardson was a brilliant mathematician. He was brought up as a Quaker and remained one throughout his life. At the outbreak of the First World War he declared himself a conscientious objector but, in 1916, went to

France having joined the Friends Ambulance Unit. While there he spent his few rest periods working on his ideas of mathematical predictions. He joined the Met Office at the end of the war but his Quaker stance forced him to leave in 1920 when the Met Office came under Air Ministry control. In 1922 he published *Weather Prediction by Numerical Processes*. This centred on the need for computing power. By "computers", he meant, of course, humans. He developed a somewhat tongue in cheek vision of a Great Forecast Factory which he saw as rather like a theatre with tiers of workers covering all areas of the globe studying the observations sent to them and then bringing their results to a central point where forecasts were derived. He calculated that 64,000 of these human computers would be required! But included in his scheme was the idea of dividing the atmosphere into grid boxes, which is at the core of modern computer-based forecasting. He fully understood the complexity of the problem, comparing it to London and saying: "London has more going on than anyone can attend to". He wrote a further paper; *Mathematical equations that determine the risk of war* and then moved into teaching at schools and colleges. We had to wait until the 1960s for the advent of electronic computers to bring his factory to reality.

Attempts were made in the early 1920s to assess the accuracy of forecasts made using NWP techniques compared with those of Met men who relied on their training and experience to draw inferences from synoptic charts. No clear outcomes resulted. Gordon Dobson (1889-1976) was involved in this work, and in several areas of meteorology. He cooperated for a time with William Dines and later with Frederick Lindeman, who was to become Churchill's wartime scientific advisor. Dobson is, however, best known for furthering our understanding of the ozone layer, that crucial barrier to ultraviolet rays that can be so harmful to our skins. He was a skilled instrument maker; as a young man he had constructed a machine to measure waves on Lake Windermere. His major breakthrough was in designing a spectrophotometer, which measures UV and is still in use today. It was this invention that helped identify the massive hole in the ozone layer, which caused such alarm in the early 1980s. The result was the Montreal Protocol of 1987 that halted the use of CFCs. This international agreement was unprecedented; the fear is that it might prove to be unique. There is limited evidence that efforts to tackle the problems of a changing climate will be equally successful.

BETWEEN THE WARS – THE DEMANDS OF AVIATION

The major innovations introduced during the First World War formed the basis of forecasting in the inter-war years. Thus the 1920s and 1930s were more a time of improving the organisation of weather forecasting across the globe rather than making any advances in forecasting itself. The speed with which fixed wing flying developed was dramatic. A mere sixteen years elapsed between the first flight by the Wright Brothers in 1903 to the first transatlantic flight, by Alcock and Brown, in 1919. Just ten years later speeds of over 340 mph were achieved in the Schneider Trophy races flown round a circular course. By this time, Air Mail flights were a regular feature of life in the United States. European air fleets were in fierce competition while routes to all parts of the British Empire had been surveyed and activated.

The central meteorological problem was how to get take-off, in-flight and landing information to aircraft which still had relatively short endurance. The availability of radiotelephony, following Marconi's transmission of a trans-Atlantic signal from Poldhu in Cornwall to Newfoundland, was an indispensable method of communication. However, organisational problems abounded. Common systems had to be agreed, reporting stations had to be set up. As important, some method of reviewing the weather to see if it was wise to take off, to continue a flight once started or to land was required. One such system concerned "fit to fly" standards. These were proposed by some authorities as mandatory weather rules, which would permit or forbid flights to take place. Most aviators resisted any such moves, deeming, often with some justification, that they knew best. We may note, referring to airship flying which has been covered above, that following such rules would almost certainly have avoided the loss of the R101. However, commercial competition overruled the idea of any such restrictions.

None of this is to say that significant developments in meteorology to aid the aviator did not take place. In France in 1929 Robert Bureau (1892-1965) introduced radiosonde balloons for measuring upper air conditions. Their value was based on the experience of kite launching and of manned and unmanned balloon flights with meteographs attached that had been in use from the turn of the century.

Fig 12. WRENS launching a Radiosonde balloon, 1942

It was their use that led to the advances in upper air meteorology achieved by Rossby in his work in the United States in the late 1920s and 1930s, which are covered in the section concerning the jet stream.

THE SECOND WORLD WAR

The Second World War saw massive strides made in weather forecasting. The need, indeed necessity, for accurate forecasting permeated every theatre of war and every operation, large or small. Two, relatively well known examples, are given here. The case of *Typhoon Cobra* is one and the D-Day landings the other.

The US fleet in the Pacific was involved in many protracted operations against the Japanese Navy. This required the Fleet to make frequent rendezvous with supply ships and refuelling tankers. One such meeting took place in December 1944 between a Replenishment at Sea group and Task Force 38 under the command of the charismatic Admiral Halsey, some 300 miles east of Luzon in the Philippines. TF 38 was struck by *Typhoon Cobra* and instead of dispersing remained together since the need for refuelling was becoming critical. An attempt was made to outrun the cyclone, but, in error, the Force sailed into the heart of the storm. Three destroyers and almost 800 crewmembers were lost, as well as over 100 aircraft that were wrecked or washed overboard. The track of the storm followed a predictable course, but this was not realised. The Admiral was exonerated at the subsequent inquiry. Perhaps, had Piddington's hornbook been on the bridges of the ships, the disaster might have been averted.

The D-Day landings were the most complex and most risky operations of the Second World War. Three teams of meteorologists were involved in advising General Eisenhower on the wisdom, or otherwise, of proceeding with the invasion on the pre-planned date of 5th June. The RAF team was led by Group Captain James Stagg (1900-1975) with the support of two experienced forecasters, one of whom was Charles Douglas, already mentioned for his work in the First World War, and the other was Sverre Pettersson who had graduated from the Bergen School. The American team, led by Irving Krick, relied mainly on the use of analogue charts comparing past and current weather and extrapolating forecasts from them. The British team were more used to considering weather arriving from across the Atlantic. There was also a team from the Admiralty who were particularly concerned about actual landing condition on the beaches. It is hardly surprising that differences arose between the teams, though these were sometimes unnecessarily acrimonious. The American team pressed for the invasion to go ahead as planned. The RAF team disagreed strongly, but did offer the hope of an improving situation the following day when a ridge of high pressure was likely to extend further north towards Europe. Eisenhower accepted their advice and postponed D-day until 6th June. Had the invasion gone ahead on 5th June it would almost certainly have been a total disaster. Following the invasion, Krick spoke in America and publically offered a very distorted picture of the roles of the three teams suggesting a lack of "press-on spirit" among the British; this, even though their forecast had been correct. Pettersson in particular was incensed by this slur and was disappointed that Stagg did not immediately rebut it. Indeed, Stagg's book *Forecast for Overlord* barely mentions the matter. Unpleasant bickering followed, but was, perhaps happily, lost in the glow of success that surrounded the invasion. It is noteworthy that, had the operation been delayed by two weeks, which was the alternative to June 6th, easterly gales would almost certainly have led to disaster. They were strong enough to wreck one of the massive Mulberry Harbours that had to be towed across the channel and on which resupply to the front line absolutely depended.

THE JET STREAM

By the end of the war, pressure charts for the upper air levels of 500 and 200 millibars were regularly being produced. However, the importance of the jet stream appears to have slipped under the radar. The northern polar jet is now seen as playing a crucial role in weather patterns right around the northern hemisphere. The full impact of this meandering ribbon of fast-moving air, which marks the boundary between upper air masses of very different temperatures, was not realised by the military until the end of the War. Its existence, however, was known of well before this time. William Ley (1840-1896), a Vicar from Leicestershire, made an extensive study of cirrus clouds, which could sometimes be seen moving as fast as 150 mph. He noted that storms were often preceded by this forewarning. The Japanese meteorologist Wasaburo Oishi (1874-1950) had also observed and reported on the existence of very high wind speeds in the upper reaches of the troposphere during the early 1920s. He sought the widest possible readership for his work and selected Esperanto as the best language to achieve this. Not surprisingly, it was read by very few. However, in Japan, knowledge of the jet stream did lead to the use of balloon bombs in the Second World War. These were launched from Japan to be carried high above the Pacific to the United States where the balloon exploded, dropping its bombs. Virtually no damage was caused by these attacks but their use became part of the post-war debate on unrestricted aerial warfare.

In Europe, RAF Fighter Command's so-called "Worst Day of the War" took place in 1943 when a whole squadron of Spitfire aircraft was lost. The Squadron was formed of American pilots who had originally joined the RAF at the start of the War. When the United States entered the War they were brought together to form the Eagle Squadron. For their first operation they had taken off from Plymouth to escort bombers attacking the German U-Boat pens on the Brest Peninsular. Orbiting above complete cloud cover while waiting to rendezvous with the bombers, they were blown south across Brittany at close to 200 mph. They failed to meet up with the bombers and when they descended towards what they thought was the south coast of England, they met the full force of the Nazi defences around Lorient. Not a single aircraft survived. This major blow can be put down directly to lack of knowledge of the jet stream.

For the United States Army Air Force the failure of their much-vaunted Norden bombsight in some raids over Japan caused great consternation. The bombsight, excellent in many ways, could not cope with cross winds of the magnitude of the jet stream. It took some time for the authorities to accept that the failure to release bombs was not down to the incompetence of the crews but rather to a meteorological phenomenon, which had been noted many years previously.

There are four global jet streams, two in each hemisphere. A full understanding of the wave-like motion of the polar jet stream had to wait until some time after the war had ended. In the late 1920s Carl-Gustaf Rossby (1898-1957), yet another product of the

Bergen School, started working in America. He made a major step forward by applying the theories of fluid dynamics to the atmosphere. He was able to depict the track of the polar jet stream with its four to six meanders around the globe in what are now known as Rossby Waves. His studies of many forms of wave motion helped lay firmer foundations for the study of a whole range of patterns of oscillation. Rossby, as with many scientists, was drawn into the military at the start of the Second World War. One of his roles was to introduce the Bergen School theories to US military aviation. Strangely, the US Weather Bureau did not fully accept frontal theory until 1940 whereas the US Navy had done so from the late 1920s. When this was realised, there was both embarrassment and annoyance and a stop was put to this anomaly, with the adoption of the Bergen system by all parties.

UNSUNG HEROES

All wars produce many unsung heroes. A group of these, seldom mentioned, were the weather forecasters stationed at the thousands of air bases covering many parts of the globe. Those who worked in the United Kingdom merit special mention. They were certainly sent, at regular intervals, the synoptic chart data from central authorities. For some, especially on those bases involved in the continuing operations of Bomber Command, the task of the forecasters was to explain what higher authorities said the weather would be. But that aside, local conditions affecting everyday flying were of paramount importance if aircraft and crew losses were to be minimised on training and test flying. The risk of fog, the height of cloud bases, wind direction, turbulence; these factors often depended on local knowledge. Many airmen owe their lives to the understanding and dedication of the Station Met Man.

14. THE POST SECOND WORLD WAR PERIOD

Satellites – Radar – Buoys – Computers – Chaos theory

SATELLITES

The Second World War exemplifies the saying that war is the mother of invention. This may well be extended to Cold War since the period of the 1960s and 1970s saw many of those inventions converted into major scientific advances. Two of these were especially significant to weather forecasting. They were the building of rockets and radar. Based on the German V2 weapons, rockets were developed with ever increasing power and ever increasing payloads. Not just warheads, but satellites could be launched into space. And it was war, in this case the Cold War, that sustained the massive expenditure and diversion of personnel that was necessary to continue the advances in this field. The result was the first weather satellite, TIROS 1, which went into orbit in 1960. The development of TIROS was essentially a team effort. Yes, there were leaders covering the necessary disciplines but the idea of a lone thinker had been left far behind. Steady progress gave rise to satellites in polar orbit at a height of some 550 miles with the earth spinning round beneath them and those in geo-stationary orbit at about 22,000 miles rotating at exactly the same speed as the earth. The first provided a mosaic of pictures covering the whole globe and the second continuous readings but over only a small area. Natural light, infra-red and ultra violet images are now available and they have transformed our ability for both forecasting weather and for research purposes. Over 100 weather satellites have been launched and many are still in operation.

Fig 13. TIROS 1. The first weather satellite, launched in 1960

Fig 14. False colour image of cloud in the North West Atlantic

RADAR

Another invention from the Second World War that became important in the field of weather forecasting was that of radar. Robert Watson-Watt (1892-1973) struggled to overcome the effect of clouds and rain, which were a major distraction for radar operators, causing clutter on their screens and hiding the returns from aircraft. This clutter was exactly what the weather forecasters wished to see. Doppler rainfall radar is used to locate all forms of precipitation, to check its amount and see whether it is rain, hail or snow. It is now an essential tool for tracking rain-bearing clouds and forecasting where rain may fall. Inputs can be fed into computer models.

BUOYS

Buoys play a vital role in recording sea temperatures, both at the surface and also at varying depths down to the sea floor. In many ways their wide spread use was due to cold war competition, especially in gathering information for nuclear submarines, both missile launchers and attack boats. The oil industry, as it spread its drilling operations into ever-deeper water, also provided useful additional data. The value of this is seen especially in the field of proxy data as used by climatologists, where the composition of ocean cores and the wealth of foraminifera they contain reveals evidence of past temperatures and gas concentrations in the atmosphere. They also play a key part in monitoring sea temperatures in the Pacific Ocean, with the hope that this will enable more reliable forecasting of changes to the El Niño Southern Oscillation, or ENSO. There are currently about 100 moored buoys and 1000 drift buoys in operation.

COMPUTERS

Computers now play a central role in all forms of activities; weather forecasting is no exception. However, the more specific use of computer modelling of the atmosphere and oceans is now the universal method of predicting future weather and climate. Computer modelling is discussed in more detail below.

CHAOS THEORY

Edward Lorenz (1917-2008) was a mathematician and meteorologist who took an early interest in the use of computer technology to assist with weather forecasting. He adopted and adapted Vilhelm Bjorknes' set of non-linear differential equations, the so-called primitive equations which contain seven variables. Progress was promising until, during a re-run of one set of data, very minor changes in inputs had to be included since the print-out from which they were taken recorded to only three places of decimals compared with six places in the initial run. The outcome of the second run was a totally different forecast. From this sprang the idea of chaos theory which Lorenz made public in 1961 with the question: "If a butterfly flaps its wings in Brazil will it cause a tornado in Texas?" In essence Lorenz was saying that extremely small errors in in-put may, or may not, produce huge changes in output. This unhappy situation was inevitable in any complex, non-linear chaotic situation such as was found in the atmosphere. Lorenz's view was that this limited the time period of validity of any forecast to an absolute maximum of 14 days.

Before Lorenz's game changing intervention meteorologists thought they were moving towards a time when it would be possible to forecast the weather with accuracy for a considerable period ahead. This view was commonly held from the early days of the 19th century. However, with the arrival of chaos theory this certainty began to fade. By the end of the 20th century, and to the present day, we have undergone a complete shift to a position where most meteorologists admit such certainty is unattainable. Forecasts are, understandably, hedged about with caveats and reservations. Probabilities can be offered, some close to certainties, but further than that we are not able to go.

15. WITHER
WEATHER FORECASTING?

We have seen how, through the centuries, individuals have furthered the progress of weather forecasting. They have been bold enough to carry the debate into new areas, many of them being true lone thinkers. As we moved into the 20th century we have seen, throughout science, a significant shift towards team working. By the end of the Second World War a wide range of new technologies became available. Rocket science and the availability of satellite imagery in several different forms, radar and Doppler radar, deep ocean surveys, computer modelling, all of these demanded specialist knowledge and with that a whole new approach to weather analysis and forecasting. And now an ever-growing volume of data is being collected. Currently over one million observations are made each day worldwide. The exploitation of all these technologies and all this data demands an international, multi-disciplinary approach. The Intergovernmental Panel on Climate Change offers a good example of how such cooperation can work. It is unlikely that one individual, one polymath could command the detail of this array of technologies so that they could join the masterminds of the past. Yet might we not sometimes pause and, looking back, wonder if much the same might have been said of those whose grasp of so many disparate subjects we so admire?

We may note, too, that some talented scientific publicists and commentators may become household names. Nor should their roles be too readily dismissed as they help to promote both our understanding and our wonder at the complexities of meteorology. In this age of graphic design they may bring with them new forms of displays to help the layman better understand this science. Is it too far-fetched to suggest that from that might spring our future heroes?

Computers and computer modelling clearly play a central role in forecasting. From the ENIAC computer in 1950 until today, vast strides have been made. Thus computer modelling is now seen by many as the only game in town. Yet it is subject to many limitations. It can instil a false sense of assurance while still requiring the simplification of data. It is always subject to input errors where even minor variations can result in major inaccuracies in outcomes. Bigger, and ever more expensive, computers seem able to inch effectiveness forward though in the United Kingdom we may, at times, question even that rate of progress. And large computers themselves are reaching a point where greater speed and size begin to bring unacceptable penalties. These have to be added to the problems inherent in the methodology. A way to try to limit some of these shortcomings was proposed in 1969 by the American Edward Epstein

(1931-2008) who filled a number of senior posts including Director of the National Climate Program. He encouraged the use of ensemble models. In essence this meant taking the outputs from a range of models which used very slightly different inputs. This method eases one problem only to introduce another. Probabilities are the outcome but how well are these understood and how useful are they as guides to action? These difficulties are well illustrated in the United States where many organisations are involved in forecasting tropical storm and hurricane tracks. A bewildering complexity of wriggling lines is the result showing how much progress is still to be made. And chaos theory remains the elephant in the room.

These various constraints give rise to a number of questions. How likely is it that some overarching, all embracing law of weather exists and if so, how likely is it that it can be found? Might it lie within some interaction between troposphere and stratosphere as in sudden stratospheric warming? Or is it to be found in the ocean and air interface producing some form of tele-connected oscillations? Might better understanding of the sun as the prime driver of all our weather provide us with an over-arching law? Or is some new form of mathematics waiting for the right person to help us see the various linkages between the many elements of the weather?

There remains the nostalgic backward glance to those great weathermen of the past. As the fog of the present is slowly dispersed by time, we may be able to pick out the shadowy figures behind the advances we make. We retain a lingering hope that Einstein might have been right when he said, "Only daring speculation can lead us forward, and not the accumulation of facts". For now, the idea of the Weatherman is obsolete. Perhaps, at the right time, and in the right place, a daring speculator may arise to state what we would then declare to be self-evident about a law of weather. That weather, and how all its elements interrelate, will continue to surprise and elude us, but also delight and enthral us – which is as well since our very lives depend on it.

ANNEX

Loss of Ships at Sea in the 19th Century

Many factors led to the appalling loss of life in shipwrecks in the 19th century. High on the list is the approach of ship owners to their responsibilities to their crews. A brief résumé of how those responsibilities were exercised is relevant to the story of the Weathermen and those among them who sort to predict when storms might put vessels and their crews at risk.

In 1807 *HMS Snipe* was riding out a storm in the roads at Great Yarmouth. She was struck by another ship, whose anchor chain had parted, and she ran aground. The ship, all the crew and a considerable number of French prisoners of war were lost. George Manby (1765-1854) was among a large crowd that watched helplessly as the *Snipe* broke up. He resolved to find a way of getting a line aboard a stricken ship to enable sailors and passengers to be hauled ashore. The result was the Manby Mortar, which fired a light line across a ship and allowed a heavier line to follow. The Breeches Buoy was then introduced to facilitate the process. It is estimated that over 130 lives were saved in the first few years of operation by using the mortar.

The unstinting work of Sir William Hillary in setting up the Institute for the Preservation of Life at Sea from Shipwreck – which became the RNLI in 1854 – resulted in many lifeboat stations being set up around the coast. And the need was great indeed. In the late 1850s almost 1,000 lives were lost at sea each year. Voluntary donations played an important part in the purchase of many of the boats; it was indicative of the great ground swell of concern for this loss of life, which directly or indirectly affected so many people.

One approach to tackling the problem required continuing and detailed survey work since it was not only in times of storms that ships were lost. But what of the responsibilities of ship owners? In the United Kingdom the story of consistent, and successful, attempts to block legislation to control the merchant fleet of what claimed to be the greatest maritime nation in the world makes depressing reading. Different rules existed for passenger and cargo ships. For the latter there was no requirement to provide any lifeboats. Any sailor who had signed up to sail and then refused to go to sea because they considered the vessel unseaworthy could be, and was, imprisoned. It is estimated that some 1,500 men were treated in this way.

So what was the condition of many of the ships? This was a boom time for shipping and it was said that from 1850 to 1870 not a single ship was scrapped; many in a poor condition were repainted, renamed and sent back to sea. Some were heavily insured in the near certainty that they would not be able to complete a single voyage. Not without reason were they called coffin ships. Colliers were particularly at risk. They were heavily stressed during loading and unloading and it was a simple matter to overload them. The case of the *Lovely Nelly* was typical. In 1861 her captain refused to take her to sea. The first mate, though with no appropriate qualifications, was promoted captain. The collier set sail from Sunderland to London in what was clearly a seriously overloaded condition. She soon turned back, having sprung a leak. At this point she was struck by a severe storm and wrecked. Due to the prodigious efforts of a lifeboat crew, all bar one of those on board were saved. Some years later the newly appointed "captain" qualified to sail – as a first mate!

In February 1871 a total of nearly 400 Newcastle colliers were wind-bound in Bridlington Bay. The wind direction then changed and many set sail. However, a fierce storm then struck them and a total of twenty-eight ships were wrecked. Over eighty lives were lost including six lifeboat men. Even as this news spread, so did the resistance to any change in legislation stiffen among the owners, many of whom were MPs. It was not until 1876 that the Merchant Shipping Act was finally passed. This required the use of the Plimsoll Line to ensure ships were not overloaded. The final introduction of this feature does great credit to Samuel Plimsoll (1824-1898) who fought tirelessly for the safety of those who went down to the sea in ships.

BIBLIOGRAPHY

Anderson, K., 2005. *Predicting the Weather.* Chicago: University of Chicago Press

Binney, R., 2010. *Wise Words and Country Ways.* Newton Abbot: David and Charles

Buchan, A., 1867. *Handy Book of Meteorology.* London: William Blackwood

Burton, J., 1986. *Robert FitzRoy and the Early History of the Meteorological Office.* British Journal for the History of Science Vol 19 No 2

Collins, P., 2007. *FitzRoy and his Barometers.* Trowbridge: Baros Books

Courtney, N., 2002. *Gale Force 10.* London: Review

Crewe, M., 2002. *Meteorology and Aerial Navigation.* Occasional paper published by the Royal Meteorological Society

Defoe, D., 2005. *The Storm* London: Penguin Books

Eden, P., 2008. *Great British Weather Disasters.* Continuum UK

Eyewitness Companions. 2008. *Weather.* London: Dorling Kindersley Ltd

Fagan, B., 2000. *The Little Ice Age.* New York: Basic Books

Fagan, B., 2004. *The Long Summer.* London: Granta Books

FitzRoy, R., 1859. *Barometer and Weather Guide.* London: Eyre and Spotteswoode

FitzRoy, R., 1863. *The Weather Book*. London: Longman

Fort, T., 2006. *Under the Weather*. London: Century

Golanski, J., 2007. *British Weather and the Climate of Enlightenment*. Chicago: University of Chicago Press

Gribben, J & M., 2003. *FitzRoy*. London: Headline Books

Halford, P., 2004. *Storm Warning*. Stroud: Sutton Publishing Ltd

Hamblyn, R., 2001. *The Invention of Clouds*. London: Picador

Hanson, J., 2009. *Storms of my Grandchildren*. London: Bloomsbury Publishing Plc

Harris, A., 2015. *Weatherland*. London: Thames and Hudson

Holden, C & L., 1988. *Life and Death on the Royal Charter*. Chester: Calgo Publications

Lamb, H., 1995. *Climate History and the Modern World*. London: Routledge

Lovelock, J., 1979. *Gaia*. Oxford: Oxford University Press

MacBayne, R., 2002. *The Greatest Storm*. Stroud: Sutton Publishing Ltd

Mellersh, H., 1968. *FitzRoy of the Beagle*. London: Rupert Hart-Davis Ltd

Moore, P., 2015. *The Weather Experiment*. London: Chatto and Windus

Parker, G., 2013. *Global Crisis*. Yale: Yale University Press

Pettersson, S., 1941. *Introduction to Meteorology*. New York: McGraw-Hill

Reid, W., 1838. *Attempt to Develop the Law of Storms by means of Facts*. London: John Weale

Rowell, G., 1840-1889. *Electric Meteorology*. Various papers available through Lightning Source UK, Milton Keynes

Shaw, N., 1913. *Forecasting Weather*. London: Constable and Co

Stagg, J., 1971. *Forecast for Overlord*. Shepperton: Ian Allen Ltd

Steinmetz, A., 1866. *Weathercasts and Storm Prognostics*. London: John Routledge and Sons

Thompson, H., 2005. *This Thing of Darkness*. London: Headline

Walker, G., 2007. *An Ocean of Air*. London: Bloomsbury Publishing

Woodham-Smith, C., 1958. *The Reason Why*. London: Penguin Books

Wulf, A., 2015. *The Invention of Nature*. London: John Murray

GENERAL INDEX

INDEX OF NAMES

ABOUT THE AUTHOR

Gordon Tripp was in the RAF for many years, flying as a navigator and later as a tutor at the RAF Staff College. He completed a tour in Nigeria, leading a team that assisted the Nigerian Air Force in setting up their own Staff College. He then worked for a developing world charity, seeing how changes in the climate were impacting on the world's poor. He has given talks and run courses on the weather and climate for several years.